Nonfiction Comprehension

Reading Strategies for the Content Areas

www.harcourtschoolsupply.com
2
Contents

Nonfiction Comprehension: Grades 3–4, SV 8947-8

Students learn much about their world through reading. Fiction, through illustration, tells them about people and human nature. Nonfiction, through information, tells them what the world is like. Just as certain skills are needed to gain a deeper understanding of fiction, so are certain skills needed to gain the most from nonfiction. The purpose of this book is to help teachers to pass on those nonfiction skills to young readers so they can move from learning to read to reading to learn.

As students progress through the grades, their reading load increases and changes. Students may encounter an increased volume of text. They may have to deal with new vocabulary and new concepts in each content area. They may lack prior knowledge to apply to new information. They may have a basic unfamiliarity with expository text features. They may be asked to show their understanding of nonfiction selections on standardized tests. This book includes reading selections and techniques to help teachers to overcome these common hurdles that students face.

This book is especially appropriate for:

- Reading teachers who want to provide extra nonfiction practice using specific comprehension skills;

- Teachers in other disciplines who want to reinforce content-specific comprehension skills;

- Parents who want to provide extra nonfiction reading practice for their child.

A **good reader** is a **good learner**. The goal of this book is to **make all students good readers!**

Use and Organization

Research suggests that "explicit teaching techniques are particularly effective for comprehension strategy instruction. In explicit instruction, teachers tell readers why and when they should use strategies, what strategies they should use, and how to apply them. The steps of explicit instruction typically include direct explanation, teacher modeling ("thinking aloud"), guided practice, and application." (*Put Reading First*, p. 53)

This book includes two types of teacher information pages. The book is divided into six units that identify major comprehension areas. These units are further divided into 16 specific comprehension skills. At the beginning of each unit is a teacher information page that identifies the comprehension skills in that unit and provides background details and recognition strategies for each skill. Each comprehension skill is then covered in a lesson that includes reading selections from a variety of content areas. At the beginning of each lesson is another teaching information page that covers the reading selections in the lesson. Summaries of each selection are provided, along with vocabulary words and writing exercises. Included on this page are approaches to tap prior knowledge, emphasize and reinforce the comprehension skill, preview text features, and help students to comprehend the selection.

Each lesson contains one to three reading selections that emphasize a specific comprehension skill, such as summary or comparison-contrast. Many of the reading selections also contain visual aids that the student can use to gain extra information about the topic. A unit on visual aids prepares the student for the use of these tools. Each reading selection also includes activities that center on comprehension and vocabulary. At the back of the book are a complete answer key and a variety of graphic organizers.

TECHNIQUES
to Improve Comprehension

This book offers a variety of comprehension techniques on the teacher information pages. Here are more comprehension techniques that can be used to increase student comprehension.

- Introduce the reading skills of skimming and scanning. Skimming notes the general subject and major headings. Scanning looks for key words.

- Model a fluent reading process: read; stop and think; reread when comprehension breaks down.

- Ask questions that help relate the reading selection to the reader's experiences, emotions, or knowledge.

- Use comparison-contrast to help the students to connect new information to known information.

- Model and require students to create questions about their reading.

- Use graphic organizers to organize and display group thinking, questioning, and learning.

- Help the students to draw conclusions from information the author has provided. Help the students to question their way through the selection.

- Have the students summarize the main points of each selection or section of the reading.

- Provide ways for the students to record changes in their thinking as new information is gathered.

Bibliography

Armbruster, B. B., F. Lehr, and J. Osbourne. *Put Reading First: The Research Building Blocks for Teaching Children to Read.* Washington, D. C.: National Institute for Literacy, 2001.

Skill	Mathematics	Biography	History	Economics	Geography	Earth Science	Life Science	Physical Science	Daily Skills
Diagrams							9, 51, 53	7, 9	
Graphs	12, 14		12		12, 14				
Charts	17					14	17		17, 29
Maps	20				20, 83, 106	20, 84	54		20
Main Idea		43, 73	43, 73	25, 35	24, 31, 37	24, 31, 37	9, 24, 71	7	37
Details					31	31			28, 29, 35
Summary				35	37	37	53		37
Narration of Event		43, 45	43, 45						
Narration of Process	49					49	51, 53		
Cause-Effect		63	63		59	59	61		
Description		73	73				69, 71		
Division						79	76		
Classification			83		83	83	87		
Comparison-Contrast	90			25			91		
Drawing Conclusions		43, 45, 102, 112	43, 45, 102, 106, 112	106	31, 84, 100, 106, 114	31, 79, 84, 100	53, 71, 76, 114		
Fact or Opinion?		112	112		114		114		

UNIT 1

Visual Aids

We all know the old saying, "A picture is worth a thousand words." The saying is true for visual aids, which includes graphic organizers. These graphic sources range from simple illustrations to complicated graphs and charts. Often, graphic sources such as diagrams, graphs, charts, and maps are skipped over by young readers because they look hard to understand. These visual aids are not hard to understand if students take the time to study them. These graphic sources can give more information in a smaller space than the written word.

• Diagrams (Lesson 1)

A diagram is an illustration that is meant to explain rather than represent. It does not try to show the reader what the thing looks like. Instead, it breaks the topic into its parts and arrangement. For example, a diagram of a food chain would show all the members of the chain. It would use arrows to show the arrangement or relationship between the members. Diagrams are very helpful in explaining mathematical or scientific topics.

To understand a diagram:
- Read the title of the diagram or article carefully. What is it about?
- Read all of the labels. Take time to figure out what they mean.
- If the diagram has a caption, read the caption carefully.
- If arrows are used in the diagram, study the movement suggested by the arrows.
- Try to identify all the parts and their relationship to one another.

• Graphs (Lesson 2)

A graph is a diagram that uses pictures, points, lines, bars, or areas to show and compare information. A pictograph uses pictures to show information. A bar graph uses bars, and a line graph uses one or more lines to give information. A pie graph uses slices of a round graph to show facts.

To understand a graph:
- First, identify the kind of graph.
- Read the title of the graph carefully. What information does the graph show?
- Read the labels on the side and bottom of the graph. Take time to figure out what they mean.
- Follow the bars or lines with your finger.
- Move a finger from the labels to the point on the line or bar to get the information you need.

• Charts (Lesson 3)

A chart is used to present exact information in an orderly way. Tell the students they use charts every day, such as menus, bus schedules, and TV schedules. Charts arrange facts in a way that makes them easy to read and understand. Often, charts include times or numbers.

To understand a chart:
- Read the title of the chart carefully.
- Read all the labels in the chart. Decide what the labels mean.
- Read the times or numbers in the chart.
- Use your finger to follow the rows or columns.
- Be sure you know what information you need and what information the chart gives.

• Maps (Lesson 4)

Maps are used to give information about a place. Maps are like a drawing of a place from above. Maps can tell about the boundaries of places. They can tell about the landscape, the climate, or the population. Most maps have the same features, such as a compass rose, a legend or key, and a distance scale.

To understand a map:
- Read the title of the map. What information does the map give?
- Find the compass rose. Run your finger along the points of the rose. Usually, north is toward the top of the map.
- Find the distance scale. Practice measuring a distance on the map.
- Find the legend or key. Look at all the symbols. Take time to figure out what they mean.
- Find some of the symbols on the map.
- Study the map to find the information you need.

Unit 1: Teacher Information
Nonfiction Comprehension: Grades 3–4, SV 8947-8

Diagrams

Tap Prior Knowledge

Ask the students if they have ever seen pictures that show how to assemble a toy. Those pictures are diagrams.

"Color": Ask students if they have ever seen a rainbow. The rainbow is a prism that splits sunlight into the spectrum of colors.

"The Eye and Sight": Ask students if they have ever visited an eye doctor for a checkup. What did the doctor do? Ask students if they have ever used a camera. Cameras work much like the eye.

Skill to Emphasize

Review the section about diagrams on page 5. Point out the diagrams in the selections.

Preview Text Features

Point out the diagrams in the articles. Point out the caption under the diagram in "Color." The caption gives additional information about the diagram. Boldfaced words indicate vocabulary words.

Comprehending the Selection

You may wish to model how to identify the main idea in each selection by asking: *What is this article mostly about?* Ask the students how the diagrams help them to learn more about the topic.

Reinforce the Comprehension Skill

Remind the students that a diagram is an illustration that is meant to explain. It breaks the topic into its parts and arrangement. Ask the students how the diagrams in each selection show the parts and arrangement of the parts.

Assess

Have the students complete the activities for each selection.

Have the students draw a diagram that helps to explain a topic they have studied recently in science.

Have the students search through the newspaper or news magazines for diagrams and bring these diagrams to school to share with the class.

SELECTION DETAILS

Summary

"Color" (page 7): Light is a mixture of all colors. A prism can be used to split light into the spectrum of seven colors.

"The Eye and Sight" (page 9): The eye is a sense organ that gathers light and converts the light to pictures. These pictures are then sent to the brain, which understands the pictures.

Selection Type
Nonfiction Science Articles with Diagrams

Comprehension Skill
Use Visual Aids for Information

Standards
Reading
- Identify main idea and details.
- Use a variety of appropriate reference materials, including representations of information such as diagrams, maps, and charts, to gather information.
- Identify details in a reading selection.

Science
- Explore light and color.
- Explore the parts of the eye and sight.

VOCABULARY

Introduce the vocabulary words and write them on the board. Help students find a definition for each word. Have students use each word in a sentence.

"Color"
absorbs	wavelength
reflected	spectrum
prism	

"The Eye and Sight"
iris	pupil
lens	optic nerve

Color

Every day, you see objects of many different colors. The objects do not really have colors. The colors come from light. An object has a certain color because of the way it **absorbs** light.

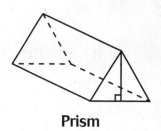

Prism

Sunlight is a mixture of light of all colors. Each color of light has a different **wavelength**. Red light has a long wavelength. Violet light has a short wavelength.

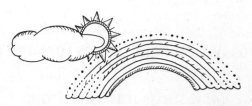

The different colors of light can be seen in a rainbow.

A red object, such as an apple, absorbs all colors of light except red. The red light is **reflected**. You see a red apple. White objects reflect all colors of light. Black objects absorb all colors of light.

The **spectrum** is all the colors of light. You can see the spectrum by using a **prism**. A prism is a piece of glass shaped like a triangle. When light passes through the prism, it is separated into all its different colors. The spectrum can also be seen in a rainbow. Rainbows happen when the sun shines after it has been raining. The drops of water in the sky act like tiny prisms to separate out the different colors of sunlight.

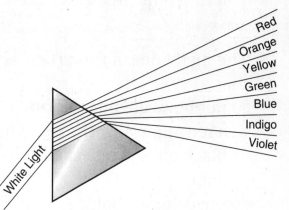

When light passes through a prism, it is separated into its different colors.

Comprehension and Vocabulary Review

→ **Darken the circle by the best answer.**

1. Sunlight is ____.
   Ⓐ cold
   Ⓑ a mixture of light of all colors
   Ⓒ a mixture of snow and fire
   Ⓓ made of glass

2. When light passes through a prism, ____.
   Ⓐ it turns into raindrops
   Ⓑ it becomes an apple
   Ⓒ it is separated into different colors
   Ⓓ it turns the prism into glass

3. The main idea of this article is that ____.
   Ⓐ rainbows are not colorful
   Ⓑ a red apple absorbs red light
   Ⓒ black objects reflect all colors of light
   Ⓓ the colors of objects come from light

4. An object either absorbs light or ____ light.
   Ⓐ reflects
   Ⓑ waves at
   Ⓒ rains on
   Ⓓ colors

5. Based on the diagram, the colors at the two ends of the spectrum are ____.
   Ⓐ black and white
   Ⓑ red and violet
   Ⓒ yellow and green
   Ⓓ orange and blue

6. You can conclude that a green object absorbs all colors of light except ____.
   Ⓐ red
   Ⓑ blue
   Ⓒ white
   Ⓓ green

7. A spectrum is ____.
   Ⓐ a prism
   Ⓑ all the colors of light
   Ⓒ a few colors of light
   Ⓓ red

8. A prism is ____.
   Ⓐ all the colors of light
   Ⓑ white
   Ⓒ a piece of glass shaped like a triangle
   Ⓓ hot

The Eye and Sight

Your eyes are sense organs. Remember that sense organs send different kinds of messages to the brain and the spinal cord. Your eyes send pictures of the world to your brain.

The colored part of your eye is called the **iris**. Look at the drawing of the eye and its parts. The opening at the center of the iris is the **pupil**. If there isn't much light, the pupil opens to let in more light. This makes it easier to see in dim light. In bright light, the pupil gets smaller. This protects the eye from too much light.

The **lens** of the eye can focus light to make sharp pictures. It focuses light onto the back of the eyeball. Sensory nerves cover the back of the eyeball. These sensory nerves send pictures to the **optic nerve**. The optic nerve sends the pictures to the brain. The brain understands what you see.

Your eyes are protected in many ways. The cheek and forehead bones can protect your eyes from injury. Eyelashes catch dirt and dust before they can get into your eyes. By blinking, your eyelids spread tears over your eyes. Tears help keep your eyes moist and clean.

You can help take care of your eyes. Do not rub them. You may be rubbing dirt into your eyes. Keep sharp objects away from your eyes. Wear glasses if you need them. See an eye doctor once a year to have your eyes checked.

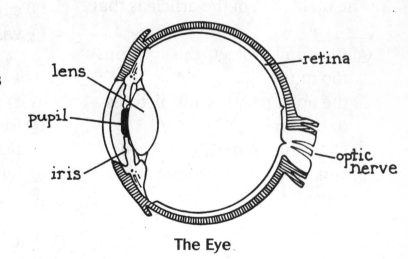

The Eye

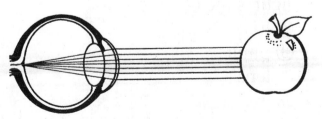

How the eye sees an apple

Nonfiction Comprehension: Grades 3–4, SV 8947-8

Comprehension and Vocabulary Review

➡️ **Darken the circle by the best answer.**

1. The colored part of the eye is the
   ____.
   - Ⓐ pupil
   - Ⓑ iris
   - Ⓒ lens
   - Ⓓ optic nerve

2. After light enters the pupil, it
   passes through the ____.
   - Ⓐ lens
   - Ⓑ brain
   - Ⓒ cheek
   - Ⓓ forehead

3. The main idea of the article is that
   ____.
   - Ⓐ the pupil protects the eye from
     too much light
   - Ⓑ the optic nerve sends pictures
     to the brain
   - Ⓒ you should not rub your eyes
   - Ⓓ your eyes are important sense
     organs

4. The optic nerve runs from the eye
   to the ____.
   - Ⓐ cheek
   - Ⓑ brain
   - Ⓒ picture
   - Ⓓ lens

5. You can conclude from the
   diagram that ____.
   - Ⓐ your iris is at the back of your
     eye
   - Ⓑ your iris is at the front of your
     eye
   - Ⓒ your pupil is on your forehead
   - Ⓓ your optic nerve is at the front
     of your eye

6. You can conclude that blinking
   ____.
   - Ⓐ is good for you
   - Ⓑ is bad for you
   - Ⓒ causes dust to get in your eye
   - Ⓓ will make your eye fall out

7. The opening that lets light into
   the eye is the ____.
   - Ⓐ iris
   - Ⓑ pupil
   - Ⓒ lens
   - Ⓓ eyelash

8. The part of the eye that focuses
   light is the ____.
   - Ⓐ iris
   - Ⓑ pupil
   - Ⓒ lens
   - Ⓓ eyelid

Nonfiction Comprehension: Grades 3–4, SV 8947-8

Graphs

Summary

"America's Largest Cities in 1776" (page 12): This bar graph shows the population of the three largest cities in America in 1776.

"Monthly Average Temperature in Denver, Colorado" (page 14): This line graph shows the average temperature in Denver throughout the year.

Selection Type
Social Studies Articles with Graphs

Comprehension Skill
Use Visual Aids for Information

Standards
Reading
- Use a variety of appropriate reference materials, including representations of information such as diagrams, maps, and charts, to gather information.

Social Studies
- Use graphs to interpret data and draw conclusions.

VOCABULARY

Introduce the vocabulary words and write them on the board. Help students find a definition for each word. Have students use each word in a sentence.

"America's Largest Cities in 1776"
population

"Monthly Average Temperature in Denver, Colorado"
temperatures   average

BEFORE READING

Tap Prior Knowledge
"America's Largest Cities in 1776": Ask students if they know how many people live in their city. Ask them how many people they think now live in the three cities named in the graph.

"Monthly Average Temperature in Denver, Colorado": Ask the students which month is the hottest in their city. Which month is the coldest?

Skill to Emphasize
Review the section about graphs on page 5. Point out the graphs in the selections.

DURING   READING

Preview Text Features
Point out that the graph in "America's Largest Cities in 1776" uses bars to compare the populations of three cities. Point out that the graph names the three cities on the side and shows the population in thousands of people on the bottom scale. Point out that the graph in "Monthly Average Temperature in Denver, Colorado" uses a line to compare the average temperature in each month in Denver. Point out the temperatures on the side of the graph and the names of the months on the bottom of the graph. Line graphs often show information over a period of time. Boldfaced words indicate vocabulary words.

Comprehending the Selection
Ask the students: *What does each graph show?* Ask the students how the graphs help them to learn more about the topic.

AFTER READING

Reinforce the Comprehension Skill
Remind the students that a graph uses bars or lines to show and compare information. Ask the students if they think graphs are a good way to show information.

Assess
Have the students complete the activities for each selection.

WRITE ABOUT IT

Have the students draw a bar graph that compares the number of boys and girls in their class.

AT HOME

Have the students search through the newspaper or news magazines for graphs and bring these graphs to school to share with the class.

America's Largest Cities in 1776

During the late 18th century, America was a growing nation. More and more people were moving to the major cities of Boston, New York, and Philadelphia. Many of the famous Americans of that time lived in these cities.

The graph on this page is a bar graph. It uses bars of different lengths to show facts. The bar graph below shows the **population** of America's three largest cities in 1776. The number of people in a city is its population.

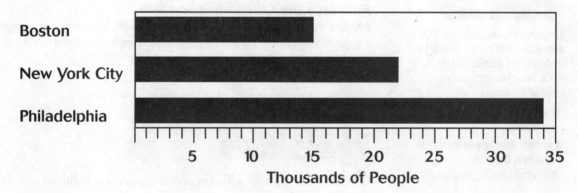

America's Largest Cities in 1776

Lesson 2: Graphs
Nonfiction Comprehension: Grades 3–4, SV 8947-8

Name _____ Date_____

Comprehension and Vocabulary Review

 Darken the circle by the best answer.

1. About what area does this map give information?
   Ⓐ Road Map
   Ⓑ Northwest Texas
   Ⓒ Mexico
   Ⓓ East Texas

2. If you drive west from Plainview through Earth, you will reach _____.
   Ⓐ Canyon
   Ⓑ Lubbock
   Ⓒ Muleshoe
   Ⓓ Amarillo

3. What direction would you travel from Amarillo to Lubbock?
   Ⓐ north
   Ⓑ south
   Ⓒ east
   Ⓓ west

4. The distance between Amarillo and Lubbock is about _____.
   Ⓐ 60 miles
   Ⓑ 100 feet
   Ⓒ 120 inches
   Ⓓ 120 miles

5. A route is _____.
   Ⓐ the bottom part of a tree
   Ⓑ a way to get from one place to another
   Ⓒ how far one place is from another
   Ⓓ a kind of park

6. Distance is _____.
   Ⓐ a way to get from one place to another
   Ⓑ a new kind of rest area
   Ⓒ how far one place is from another
   Ⓓ a direction between north and east

 Write complete sentences to answer the question.

7. Why would a road map be helpful if you were traveling in a place you did not know much about?

_____

_____

Nonfiction Comprehension: Grades 3–4, SV 8947-8

UNIT 2

Main Idea and Details

Nonfiction articles, for the most part, deal with *facts*. Writing that gives only facts is called informative writing. The writer provides details about who, what, when, where, or how. The reader of factual writing must first be concerned with details, the facts of the article.

Sometimes the writer will also ask why and then answer this question by drawing conclusions based on the facts. This kind of writing is called interpretive writing. Sometimes the reader must interpret, too. The reader may have to identify the main idea.

• Main Idea (Lesson 5)

The main idea is the main point the writer is trying to make in the article. The main idea is not always stated directly in the article. How do readers decide what the main idea of an article is? First, they have to identify the topic of the article. The main idea will be some specific comment the writer is making about the topic. Usually, each paragraph has a main idea or topic sentence. Readers can put the topic sentences together to find the main idea of the article.

The main idea cannot be a statement not supported by the article. The main idea cannot be a statement that is only a detail.

To find the main idea of an article:
- Use the Main Idea Map on page 118
- Read the article carefully.
- Find the topic of the article.
- Decide what all the sentences say about the topic.
- Ask yourself, "What is this article mostly about?"
- The title often gives a clue about the main idea.
- The main idea may be stated in the first paragraph.
- Write and revise the main idea.

Research Base

"Learning how to read informational texts involves strategies such as gathering information, summarizing and synthesizing information, and making connections to prior knowledge. Readers of informational texts must analyze where information is located within the overall organizational framework." (*Guiding Readers and Writers: Grades 3–6*, p. 400)

• Details (Lesson 6)

Details are facts that tell who, what, when, where, and how about a topic. Details add information to a story and make it more interesting. They should always support the main idea. To show their comprehension, readers are often asked to remember details from an article.

By reading carefully, readers can remember more details. By remembering more details, readers can more easily determine the main idea.

To recall specific facts and details:
- Use the Main Idea Map on page 118.
- Read the article carefully.
- Try to answer who, what, when, where, and how about the topic of the article.
- Read and think about the question carefully.
- Reread the article if necessary to answer the question.

• Summary (Lesson 7)

A summary is a short account of the main idea and key details of an article. A summary should include only the most important points in an article. Key details from the beginning, middle, and end of the article should be included. Readers must sometimes summarize an article when they need to condense the information in an article.

A good summary shows the reader's comprehension of the article's main idea and key details.

To summarize an article:
- Use the Summary Chart on page 119.
- Read the article carefully; then put it aside.
- Think about the main idea and important details.
- Write the summary without looking at the article.
- Include only the main idea and important details.
- Do include the author's name (if given) and the title of the article.
- Do not use sentences, phrases, or direct quotes from the article.
- Do not use minor details, explanations, or examples.

• Graphic Organizers
Main Idea Map	page 118
Summary Chart	page 119

Nonfiction Comprehension: Grades 3–4, SV 8947-8

Main Idea

BEFORE READING

Tap Prior Knowledge
Ask the students if they have ever eaten a banana. It was grown in another country and shipped here. Do they watch television? Their television was probably made in another country and shipped here. Many foods and products that we consume every day came from another country. They were sent here through world trade.

Skill to Emphasize
Review the section about main idea on page 22. Tell the students that they will try to find what each selection is mostly about. Have the students do the practice paragraphs before they move on to the "World Trade" reading selection.

DURING READING

Preview Text Features
Each paragraph has a topic sentence. Point out the topic sentence in each paragraph. Tell the students that if they think about all the topic sentences, they should be able to determine the main idea of the selection more easily. Boldfaced words indicate vocabulary words.

Comprehending the Selection
Model how to identify the main idea by asking: *What is this selection mostly about?*

AFTER READING

Reinforce the Comprehension Skill
Tell the students that the title of the selection often includes the topic, as in this article about world trade. The main idea is some point about the topic. What is the author saying about world trade? (that world trade has developed interdependence between countries)

Distribute copies of the Main Idea Map on page 118. Have the students complete the map for the "World Trade" article.

Assess
Have the students complete the activities for the selections.

WRITE ABOUT IT

the students write a paragraph about a product imported from another that is important to them.

HOME

ents look at items in their home. They should list where each item was ng the lists to class to share.

www.harcourtschoolsup

© Harcourt Achieve Inc. All rights r

www.harcou

© Harcourt Achi

23

Lesson 5: Teacher Information
Nonfiction Comprehension: Grades 3–4, SV 8947-8

Find the Main Idea

➡ Read the passage. Identify what it is mostly about. Darken the circle by the best answer. Then complete the Main Idea Map on page 118.

The fastest wind ever recorded was on Mount Washington in New Hampshire. In 1934, the wind blew 231 miles an hour across the top of the mountain. The wind is so fierce there that chains are anchored in solid rock to keep the weather station from blowing away.

1. This paragraph is mainly about ____.
   Ⓐ the highest mountain in the northeastern United States
   Ⓑ a weather station on the top of Mount Washington
   Ⓒ the fierce winds on the top of Mount Washington
   Ⓓ a weather station that once blew away

➡ Write a complete sentence to answer each question.

The howler monkeys of South America are very interesting animals. They hardly ever leave the treetops. When they need a drink, they lick damp leaves. The howler monkeys got their name from the noise they make when they are scared. When they sense danger, they make a loud noise that can be heard up to three miles away. Their noise can often scare away what is threatening them.

2. What is the topic of the paragraph above?

_____

_____

3. What is the main idea of the paragraph above?

_____

_____

Nonfiction Comprehension: Grades 3–4, SV 8947-8

World Trade

We live in a global **economy**. That means we get many things we want or need from other parts of the world. World trade is the movement of **goods** and **services** between countries. Goods are products that people make or grow. Services are jobs that people do to help other people. Trade between countries allows us to have things we do not produce in our country. You may watch a TV that was made in Japan and wear clothes made in China. You may eat fruit grown in Brazil.

Exports are goods and services that are produced in one country. Then, the goods and services are sent to buyers in another country. For example, the United States exports many computers to other countries.

Imports are goods and services that are produced in another country. Then, they are brought into this country and bought by people here. For example, the United States imports bananas from other countries.

World trade increases **interdependence**. Countries depend on each other to provide the things their people need or want. The more that countries trade with one another, the more interdependent they become. For example, the United States and Mexico are interdependent. The two countries trade very much with each other.

Name _____ Date_____

Comprehension and Vocabulary Review

 Darken the circle by the best answer.

1. World trade is the movement of goods and services between ____.
   Ⓐ worlds
   Ⓑ countries
   Ⓒ stores
   Ⓓ states

2. Exports are goods made in one country, then ____.
   Ⓐ sold to people in that country
   Ⓑ shipped to buyers in another country
   Ⓒ torn apart and made again
   Ⓓ thrown away

3. The main idea of this article is that ____.
   Ⓐ most countries make everything they need
   Ⓑ bananas taste good
   Ⓒ we often must get things we need from other countries
   Ⓓ many fruits are grown in Brazil

4. An economy is based on ____.
   Ⓐ money
   Ⓑ planets
   Ⓒ comets
   Ⓓ rocks

5. If you need something not made in this country, ____.
   Ⓐ you cannot have it
   Ⓑ you do not need it
   Ⓒ you must get it from another country
   Ⓓ it is probably not made

6. ____ means that people or countries must depend on each other for goods and services.
   Ⓐ Information
   Ⓑ Interdependence
   Ⓒ Independence
   Ⓓ Economy

 Write complete sentences to answer the question.

7. What is the difference between goods and services?

_____

_____

Details

BEFORE READING

SELECTION DETAILS

Summary
The sample newspaper article (page 28) gives practice in identifying the details of who, what, when, where, and how.

The Fun Park ad (page 29) gives real-life practice in identifying the details in an advertisement.

"Rivers" (page 31) presents terms associated with rivers and discusses the many ways rivers are used by people.

Selection Type
Newspaper Article
Advertisement
Social Studies Article

Comprehension Skill
Identify Details

Standards
Reading
• Identify main idea and supporting details.

Social Studies
• Study rivers and how they are used by people.

VOCABULARY

Introduce the vocabulary words for "Rivers." Write the words on the board. Help students find a definition for each word. Have students use each word in a sentence.

river	source
bed	banks
mouth	delta
tributary	

Tap Prior Knowledge
Sample newspaper article: Ask the students if they have ever read the newspaper. Newspaper articles usually tell who, what, when, where, and how.

Fun Park ad: Ask the students if they have ever read an advertisement for a fun park or other fun place. What kind of information was in the advertisement?

"Rivers": Ask the students where they think their drinking water comes from. It is possible the water comes from a river. Ask the students if they have ever fished or swum in a river. Ask the students to think of other ways that rivers can be used by people.

Skill to Emphasize
Review the section about details on page 22. Tell the students that they must pay attention to all the facts in the articles they read. Those facts are called details.

DURING READING

Preview Text Features
Each paragraph has a topic sentence. Point out the topic sentence in each paragraph. Each topic sentence is supported by detail sentences. The detail sentences give facts, or details, about the topic sentence. Boldfaced words indicate vocabulary words.

Comprehending the Selection
Model how to identify the details by asking: *What facts does the article tell about who, what, when, where, and how?*

AFTER READING

Reinforce the Comprehension Skill
Tell the students that the main idea is the general point the author is making. The details are specific facts that help the author to achieve the main idea. Ask the students to identify some of the details in the article.

Distribute copies of the Main Idea Map on page 118. Have the students complete the map for the "Rivers" article.

Assess
Have the students complete the activities for the selections.

WRITE ABOUT IT

Have the students write a paragraph about some way that they have used a river.

AT HOME

Have the students search through the newspaper or news magazines for articles about rivers and bring these articles to school to share with the class.

Name _____ Date _____

Newspaper Article

The following is a sample newspaper article. See if you can find details about who, what, when, where, and how.

Local Boy Makes Good

Luckyville—Dan Edwards, a local resident, won a new car at the mall last Wednesday. He correctly named all the Presidents of the United States. Mr. Edwards plans to drive to Washington, D.C., next summer. He said that he wants to learn more about his country.

Write a complete sentence to answer each question.

1. Who is the news article about?

_____

2. What did he do?

_____

3. When did he do it?

_____

4. Where did he do it?

_____

5. How did he do it?

_____

Nonfiction Comprehension: Grades 3–4, SV 8947-8

Name _____ Date _____

Fun Park Ad

Here is an advertisement for a new amusement park. Read the ad carefully. Pay attention to all the details. You will need them later to answer some questions.

Attention, parents and kids of all ages!

Park gates open at 10:00 A.M. on May 21! The Fun Park is open from 10:00 A.M. to 10:00 P.M. every day of the week for the whole summer!

Here are just a few of our exciting rides and amusements:

The Twist-and-Shout Roller Coaster—Swoop and soar on our brand new, thrill-packed roller coaster! Parents will be glad to know it's safe for both children and adults.

The Big Splash Water Slide—Slide into our sparkling pool. Children must be eight years or older to purchase tickets for the water slide. Life vests must be worn at all times.

Spooky Secrets Haunted House—A tour through our Spooky Secrets Haunted House will make you shiver. Children under 12 must have an adult with them.

Proud Ponies Carousel—The perfect ride for the younger children in your family. Adults can relax in a carriage built for four. The Proud Ponies Carousel is good, old-fashioned fun.

Nonfiction Comprehension: Grades 3–4, SV 8947-8

Name _____ Date _____

Comprehension Review

 Darken the circle by the best answer.

1. The amusement park will open
   on ____.
   Ⓐ May 2
   Ⓑ May 21
   Ⓒ June 6
   Ⓓ May 1

2. An eight-year-old who wants to go
   into the Spooky Secrets Haunted
   House must ____.
   Ⓐ wear a life vest
   Ⓑ buy a special ticket
   Ⓒ go with an adult
   Ⓓ wear a seatbelt

3. From the ad about the roller
   coaster, you can tell that *swoop
   and soar* means ____.
   Ⓐ stop fast
   Ⓑ go down and up
   Ⓒ cost more than the other rides
   Ⓓ go through water

4. What ride is best for young
   children?
   Ⓐ The Twist-and-Shout Roller
   Coaster
   Ⓑ Proud Ponies Carousel
   Ⓒ Spooky Secrets Haunted House
   Ⓓ The Big Splash Water Slide

5. At the end of the Big Splash Water
   Slide is a ____.
   Ⓐ house
   Ⓑ town
   Ⓒ pillow
   Ⓓ pool

6. You can tell from the passage that
   ____.
   Ⓐ some parents worry that roller
   coasters are not safe
   Ⓑ water slides may not be safe for
   all children
   Ⓒ most children at the park ride
   the roller coaster
   Ⓓ children do not like to ride the
   Proud Ponies Carousel

 Write a complete sentence to answer the question.

7. Why is the Proud Ponies Carousel fun for both parents and children?

_____

_____

Nonfiction Comprehension: Grades 3–4, SV 8947-8

Name _____   Date _____

Rivers

A **river** is a natural flow of water that runs into a lake, ocean, or other body of water. The water always flows from high ground to lower ground. The place where a river starts is called its **source**. The source may be a spring or the snow or ice on a mountain. The bottom of a river is called the **bed**, and the sides are called the **banks**. The **mouth** is the end of a river. It is the place where the river empties into another body of water. A **delta** often forms at the mouth of a large river. A delta is made of soil and sand.

Rainfall adds water to a river as it flows from its source to its mouth. When it rains, some water is soaked up by the soil. When the soil cannot soak up any more water, rain runs across the ground. It runs in small paths until it joins larger paths of water. This water is called run-off.

The water flowing in rivers is used in many ways. The water in a fast-flowing river can produce electricity. Ships on slower-moving rivers deliver food and other important materials. Many cities located along rivers get all their drinking water from rivers.

The Mississippi River is perhaps the most famous river in North America. This river is nearly 2,400 miles long. It flows from its source in northwestern Minnesota into the Gulf of Mexico. The Missouri River flows into the Mississippi River. A river that flows into another river is called a **tributary**. Long rivers usually have many tributaries. The Nile River in Africa is the longest river in the world. It is over 4,000 miles long.

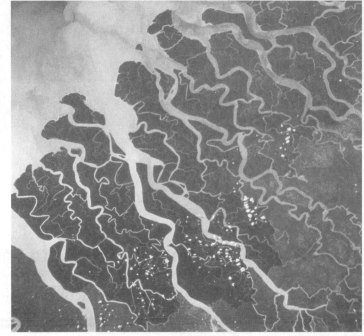

Satellite image of the mouth of the Ganges River emptying into the Bay of Bengal. This delta is the largest in the world.

Nonfiction Comprehension: Grades 3–4, SV 8947-8

Comprehension Review

 Darken the circle by the best answer.

1. The longest river in the world is
   the ____ River.
   Ⓐ Mississippi
   Ⓑ Missouri
   Ⓒ Nile
   Ⓓ Mexico

4. You can tell from the article that
   run-off ____.
   Ⓐ soaks into the ground
   Ⓑ does not soak into the ground
   Ⓒ never goes into rivers
   Ⓓ is bad for rivers

2. The Mississippi River flows from
   Minnesota to ____.
   Ⓐ Africa
   Ⓑ the Gulf of Mexico
   Ⓒ the Gulf of Missouri
   Ⓓ Mississippi

5. You can conclude that ____ water
   is needed to produce electricity.
   Ⓐ green
   Ⓑ blue
   Ⓒ fast-moving
   Ⓓ slow-moving

3. This article is mostly about ____.
   Ⓐ the Missouri River
   Ⓑ the Nile River
   Ⓒ rivers and their uses
   Ⓓ snow and ice

6. A detail about water is that it
   always flows ____.
   Ⓐ backward
   Ⓑ to the left
   Ⓒ to the right
   Ⓓ from high ground to lower
   ground

 Write complete sentences to answer the question.

7. What are some ways that rivers are useful to people?

_____

_____

_____

Name _____ Date_____

Vocabulary Review

➡ Write a vocabulary word from the box to complete each sentence.

> bed   river   banks   mouth   source   tributary

1. A _____ is a natural flow of water that runs into a lake, ocean, or other body of water.

2. The place where a river starts is its _____.

3. The sides of a river are called the _____.

4. The _____ is the end of a river.

5. A river that flows into another river is called a _____.

6. The bottom of a river is called the _____.

Just for Fun

➡ Answer the riddle.

7. Where did the river keep all its money?

_____

Summary

SELECTION DETAILS

Summary

"Taxes and Fees" (page 35) tells how the government collects the money it needs.

"Be Prepared!" (page 37) explains how to stay safe during various natural disasters.

Selection Type

Social Studies Articles

Comprehension Skill

Summarize Information

Standards

Reading
- Summarize the main information in a nonfiction text.

Social Studies
- Explore the different ways a government collects the money it needs to operate.
- Describe physical system changes such as climate and weather and safety precautions associated with such changes.

VOCABULARY

Introduce the vocabulary words for "Be Prepared!" Write the words on the board. Help students find a definition for each word. Have students use each word in a sentence.

disaster	*prone*
interior	*crouch*
shelter	*appliances*
wind-chill factor	*prevent*

Tap Prior Knowledge

"Taxes and Fees": Ask the students how they think governments get the money they need to operate. Ask the students if they have ever had to pay sales tax for a purchase.

"Be Prepared!": Ask the students if they have ever been in an earthquake, a thunderstorm, or a blizzard. What was it like? What are some ways people can stay safe in a natural disaster?

Skill to Emphasize

Review the section about summary on page 22. Tell students that a summary leaves out the unimportant ideas and details. A good summary is short and to the point. The title and headings in an article can help students to write a good summary.

DURING READING

Preview Text Features

Preview the "Be Prepared!" article with students. Call attention to some useful text features in the article, such as the section headings and lists. Model how to use these features to get the most from the article. The headings tell what each section is about. The lists are tips related to the sections. Boldfaced words indicate vocabulary words.

Comprehending the Selection

Model how to summarize the article by asking: *What are the important ideas and details in this article?*

AFTER READING

Reinforce the Comprehension Skill

Tell the students that a good summary is short and includes only the most important ideas in the article. Have the students summarize each section of the "Be Prepared!" article; then have them offer summaries for the whole article. Distribute copies of the Summary Chart on page 119. Have the students complete the chart for the "Be Prepared!" article to help them write a summary.

Assess

Have the students complete the activities for the selections.

WRITE ABOUT IT

Have the students write about a time they were in an earthquake or storm and how they stayed safe.

AT HOME

Have the students search through the newspaper or news magazines for articles about natural disasters and bring these articles to school to share with the class.

Taxes and Fees

There are thousands of different governments in the United States. These range from the federal government to the state governments to the local governments. The local governments include city and county governments and school districts. All of these governments offer goods and services to the people. Governments pay for these goods and services by collecting taxes, charging fees, or borrowing money.

Most people pay some kind of tax every day. There are many kinds of taxes. If you buy something, you may have to pay sales tax. If you have a job, you have to pay income tax. If you own a house, you have to pay a property tax. Governments also raise money by charging fees for certain goods and services. There are many kinds of fees. You must pay a fee to get your garbage collected. If you go to the park, you may have to pay a fee to use the swimming pool. You may have to pay a fee to park a car on a public street. If you ride the bus, you may have to pay a fee.

Governments also raise money by borrowing money. They may issue bonds. People buy the bonds from the government. The government promises to repay the bonds by a certain time. One popular kind of bond is the savings bond.

If people did not pay taxes and fees, the government would not have much money. Then, many of the goods and services would not be available.

> **Write a complete sentence to answer the question.**

What are three ways that a government can raise money?

_____

_____

_____

_____

Nonfiction Comprehension: Grades 3–4, SV 8947-8

Comprehension Review

➡️ **Darken the circle by the best answer.**

1. If you have a job, you may have to pay ____.
   - Ⓐ sales tax
   - Ⓑ income tax
   - Ⓒ property tax
   - Ⓓ garbage tax

2. Governments use the money they raise to ____.
   - Ⓐ have a party
   - Ⓑ go on vacation
   - Ⓒ offer goods and services to the people
   - Ⓓ start new governments

3. The main idea of this article is that ____.
   - Ⓐ there are many governments in the United States
   - Ⓑ governments offer goods and services to people
   - Ⓒ governments raise money through taxes, fees, and bonds
   - Ⓓ you have to pay a fee to go swimming

4. A popular kind of bond is the ____.
   - Ⓐ savings bond
   - Ⓑ income bond
   - Ⓒ garbage bond
   - Ⓓ park bond

➡️ **A summary is a short statement that tells what an article is about. A summary is no more than a few sentences. Use complete sentences to write a summary of the article.**

_____

_____

_____

_____

_____

Nonfiction Comprehension: Grades 3–4, SV 8947-8

Be Prepared!

You hear a low rumbling sound. Glasses and dishes begin to fall out of the cabinets. You hear horns honking and sirens blowing. Suddenly, the ground begins to shake. Someone yells, "Earthquake!" What is the best thing to do in a natural **disaster** such as this? First, it is always most important to stay calm. Natural disasters are frightening. However, knowing a few rules for keeping safe can mean the difference between life and death.

Earthquake!

Some parts of the world are **prone** to earthquakes. What should you do in the event of such a disaster? *Drop*, *cover*, and *hold on*! If you are indoors, stay there. Hide under a heavy piece of furniture and cover your eyes with your hands or arms. If there isn't any sturdy furniture near you, move to an **interior** wall. Be sure to stay away from windows or furniture that could fall over on you. Stay indoors! Don't go outside until you are sure it is safe to exit.

Once the shaking stops, check to see if you are injured. Get to the safest place in case the shaking begins again. If it does, then you should drop, cover, and hold on again until the shaking completely stops.

Thunderstorm!

If you can hear thunder, then you are in danger of being struck by lightning. Find **shelter** inside a building or a car. A car is a safe place to go if the windows are closed. If you are inside a house, unplug any electrical **appliances**. You may leave your electric lights on, but unplug televisions, radios, and toaster ovens. Do not use the telephone.

What If . . .

You Are Outside or Asleep During an Earthquake?

- If you are outside, find a clear place away from buildings, trees, or power lines.
- *Drop* to the ground and stay there until the shaking stops.
- If you are in bed, stay there. *Cover* your head with a pillow.
- *Hold* on to something that is sturdy.

What If . . .

You Are Outside During a Thunderstorm?

- If you are in water, get to land and find shelter.
- If you are in the woods, find shelter under shorter trees.
- If you are outside, find a low, open place away from trees or poles.
- **Crouch** low to the ground and place your hands on your knees with your head between them. Don't lie flat. Lying flat would make you a larger target for lightning.

37

You Are in a Car During a Blizzard?

- Do not get out of the car and try to walk to safety.
- Tie a brightly colored cloth to the car's antenna so rescue workers can see you.
- Start the car and use the heater for ten minutes each hour. Make sure the tail pipe is clear of snow so that dangerous fumes won't come inside.
- As you sit inside the car, move your arms and legs to keep warm. Find one window that is not facing the wind. Open it slightly to let air in.

Close the blinds or shades. Any window coverings could help prevent glass from shattering inside your home. Also, remember that water attracts electricity. Don't run water from faucets. Do not take a shower or a bath.

Blizzard!

A blizzard is a winter storm with strong winds, a lot of snow, and dangerously low temperatures. One reason the temperatures feel so low is because of the **wind-chill factor**. Wind makes the temperature feel much colder. The harder the wind blows, the more heat is carried away from a person's body. This lowers the body's temperature, which can make it dangerous to stay outside. If you must go outside, wear several layers of lightweight clothing. Layers of clothing are warmer than a single heavy coat. Wear gloves or mittens on your hands and a hat over your head. These clothes will help **prevent** the loss of body heat.

Comprehension Review

➤ **Darken the circle by the best answer.**

1. People should stay away from windows during an earthquake ____.
   Ⓐ so the wind can't come inside
   Ⓑ so shattered glass won't hurt them
   Ⓒ so lightning won't strike inside
   Ⓓ because it is scary to look out

2. If you can hear thunder, you are in danger of being struck by ____.
   Ⓐ lightning
   Ⓑ a train
   Ⓒ snow
   Ⓓ an earthquake

3. The ____ makes temperatures seem even colder.
   Ⓐ thermometer
   Ⓑ sunshine
   Ⓒ wind-chill factor
   Ⓓ lightning

4. The main idea of this article is that ____.
   Ⓐ earthquakes can be scary
   Ⓑ thunderstorms can get you wet
   Ⓒ blizzards are cold
   Ⓓ a few rules can keep you safe in a natural disaster

➤ **A summary is a short statement that tells what an article is about. A summary is no more than a few sentences. Use complete sentences to write a summary of the article.**

_____

_____

_____

_____

_____

_____

_____

Nonfiction Comprehension: Grades 3–4, SV 8947-8

Vocabulary Review

➡ Write words from the box to complete the paragraph.

> **wind-chill factor**   **prevent**   **prone**   **shelter**   **disaster**

A blizzard is one kind of natural _____. Northern

1

states such as New York and Maine are _____ to blizzards.

2

During a blizzard, the _____

3

can make it dangerous to be outdoors. The best thing to do is to seek

_____ immediately. If you must go outside, wear layers of

4

warm clothing to _____ the loss of body heat.

5

Build Your Vocabulary

An **analogy** compares two pairs of words. The second pair of words must
have the same relationship as the first pair.

➡ Use a word from the box to complete each analogy.

> **appliances**   **crouch**   **interior**

6. *Outside* is to *exterior* as *inside* is to _____ .

7. *Tables* are to *furniture* as *refrigerators* are to _____.

8. *Small* is to *tiny* as *squat* is to _____.

www.harcourtschoolsupply.com **40** **Lesson 7: Summary**
Nonfiction Comprehension: Grades 3–4, SV 8947-8

UNIT 3 Narration

Narration is concerned with the sequence of events or details in time. Sometimes this sequence is presented as a plot, as in a short story or historical narrative. Sometimes the sequence is a list, as in a how-to project. The sequence usually goes from beginning to end in chronological order, just as we move through time. Many times, a strong relationship exists between events. One event may cause another event. This relationship is called cause and effect.

• Sequence (Lessons 8 and 9)

Sequence is the order of events in a narrative or process. Students should be able to retell the order of events in a narration. Some words serve as signals to show the order of events. Such words are *first*, *next*, *then*, and *finally*. Lists may also be used in a selection to show order. Often, these lists are arranged alphabetically or numerically.

• Narration of Event (Lesson 8)

Narration of event is a form that should be familiar to students. They often tell stories of what they did. They read stories of fictional characters. Both of these kinds of stories contain narration of events. So do biographies and historical occurrences. A biography tells the events in a person's life. A historical occurrence also contains a narration of events, such as the sequence of events in the Civil War.

A narration of event usually includes a sense of beginning, middle, and end. It should have a setting and at least one person or historical character. A problem is usually introduced, and some outcome to the problem is indicated. The narration of event may include some emotional impact and may include an insight or point about human nature or behavior.

To recall the sequence in a narration of event:
- Use the Sequence Chart on page 120.
- Read the title for information about the event or person.
- Read the article carefully.
- Look for signal words that show the order of events.
- Decide in what order the events occurred.
- Divide the event into beginning, middle, and end.
- Retell or write a brief list of the events in order.

• Narration of Process (Lesson 9)

Narration of process is another form that should be familiar to students. One kind of process is the how-to. A how-to can be instructional, such as how to bake a cake, or it can be informational, such as how glass is made. Some processes can be quite complicated, such as the annual migratory cycle of some animals.

A narration of process includes a series of steps that also presents a sense of beginning, middle, and end. The end should indicate the completion of the process. The process essay may also include a list of materials needed, a cautionary list of things to do and not to do, and any tips or shortcuts that will facilitate the process.

To recall the sequence in a narration of process:
- Use the Sequence Chart on page 120.
- Read the title for information about the process.
- Read the article carefully.
- Look for signal words or numbers that show the order of steps.
- Note what the end result should be.
- Retell or write a brief list of the steps in order.

• Cause and Effect (Lesson 10)

An article can tell about things that happen and why they happen. Why something happens is a cause. What happens because of it is an effect. In other words, a cause tells why an effect happens. Some words are used to signal causes and effects. The words *because* and *since* often introduce a cause. The words *therefore*, *so*, *thus*, and *as a result* often introduce an effect.

To identify causes and effects:
- Use the Cause-Effect Chart on page 121.
- Read the title for information about a cause or effect.
- Read the article carefully.
- Look for signal words that introduce a cause or effect.
- Decide which part of a sentence or paragraph is the cause and which part is the effect.
- Use that information to help answer *Why*?

• Graphic Organizers

Unit 3: Teacher Information
Nonfiction Comprehension: Grades 3–4, SV 8947-8

Narration of Event

Tap Prior Knowledge

"Wilma Rudolph: Olympic Gold Medalist": Ask the students if they like to run. Have they ever heard of the Olympics? Wilma Rudolph was one of the great runners in the Olympics.

"The Swim of a Lifetime": Ask the students how far they have swum at one time. Do they know where the English Channel is?

Skill to Emphasize

Review the section about narration of event on page 41. Tell the students that they will try to find the sequence, or order, of events in each article. An event is something that happens. A narration tells about a series of events. The events occur in a certain order, called a sequence.

DURING READING

Preview Text Features

Point out the title of each article. The titles give the students information about the important events they will read about. Point out the dialogue in both articles. These words spoken by a person in the event give information about the event. Point out the words, times, or dates that suggest the sequence in the articles. Boldfaced words indicate vocabulary words.

Comprehending the Selection

Model how to identify the sequence by asking: *What words or clues tell you the order of events?*

AFTER READING

Reinforce the Comprehension Skill

Tell the students that in most narrations of event, the sequence will be in chronological order. This means the events are presented in the article just as they happen in time. "Wilma Rudolph: Olympic Gold Medalist" does not present the events in chronological order. This article begins with the parade being held for Wilma, then tells about her success in the Olympics, then tells about her problems in childhood. The sequence then returns to the parade, so this article jumps around in time. "The Swim of a Lifetime," on the other hand, uses a chronological order to tell about Gertrude Ederle's historical swim.

Distribute copies of the Sequence Chart on page 120. Have the students complete the chart for both articles. They can use another sheet of paper if necessary.

Assess

Have the students complete the activities for the selections.

WRITE ABOUT IT

Have the students write a paragraph about some accomplishment that made them feel happy or proud.

Name _____ Date _____

Wilma Rudolph: Olympic Gold Medalist

Over 40,000 people lined the streets of Clarksville, Tennessee. "Look, here she comes!" one girl cried. "Wilma, we're proud of you!" a man yelled out. The crowd screamed and cheered as Wilma Rudolph passed. Nearly everyone in her hometown had turned out for this parade in her honor. This parade for Wilma was the first event for both white and African-American people in Clarksville, Tennessee.

The year was 1960. Wilma Rudolph, now a hero, had just returned from the Olympics in Rome, Italy. There she had become the first woman to win three gold **medals** at an Olympics. She won first place in both the 100-meter race and the 200-meter race. She also placed first with her teammates in the **relay** race.

At the parade, friends and neighbors thought about Wilma's childhood. They had watched her struggle to walk. She had had **polio** and had worn a metal leg brace. They remembered her **talent** in basketball. They remembered also her speed on the track. She had never lost a race in high school. They recalled proudly the running star she became in college. All of that had prepared Wilma for the Olympics.

Wilma smiled and waved as she saw her friends and neighbors. She was a true champion. Her first steps in life had been slow. But she had set a goal for herself. She had worked hard when it was painful to do so. Wilma Rudolph overcame her **handicap** and became an Olympic hero.

Nonfiction Comprehension: Grades 3–4, SV 8947-8

Comprehension and Vocabulary Review

➤ **Darken the circle by the best answer.**

1. Wilma Rudolph's parade took place in ____.
   Ⓐ 200-meter
   Ⓑ New York City
   Ⓒ 1960
   Ⓓ 40,000

2. After Wilma won races at the Olympics, ____.
   Ⓐ she played basketball in high school
   Ⓑ she wore a metal leg brace
   Ⓒ she ran track in college
   Ⓓ her hometown held a parade in her honor

3. The main idea of this article is that ____.
   Ⓐ running fast wins races
   Ⓑ people like to have parades
   Ⓒ setting goals can lead to success
   Ⓓ playing basketball is good for runners

4. You can tell from the article that a medal is ____.
   Ⓐ a kind of award
   Ⓑ a kind of race
   Ⓒ a kind of rock
   Ⓓ a kind of ball

5. When Wilma was a child, she had a disease called ____.
   Ⓐ talent
   Ⓑ polio
   Ⓒ struggle
   Ⓓ brace

6. You can conclude from the article that ____.
   Ⓐ Wilma did not like to run
   Ⓑ Wilma worked hard to overcome her handicap
   Ⓒ Wilma did not really win any medals
   Ⓓ Wilma played baseball in high school, too

7. A talent is ____.
   Ⓐ a special ability
   Ⓑ a long race
   Ⓒ a trick play in basketball
   Ⓓ a kind of drink

8. A handicap is ____.
   Ⓐ a kind of hat
   Ⓑ a kind of tool
   Ⓒ a physical or mental disability
   Ⓓ a special shoe

The Swim of a Lifetime

Gertrude Ederle had been swimming for almost nine hours. She was more than halfway across the English Channel. If she finished this swim, she would be the first woman ever to swim from France to England.

"It looks good," thought her trainer, Bill Burgess. He was riding in a tugboat next to 18-year-old Trudy, as Gertrude was called. Suddenly he saw a huge wave hit her. She stopped swimming. Her head went underwater. "Help her!" Burgess called wildly to one of his men. "She's going to drown!"

Instantly the man swam to Trudy and grabbed her. "I was just stopping to get the salt water out of my mouth," Trudy cried. But it was too late. To make an **official** swim across the Channel, a swimmer could not be touched by anyone along the way.

The English Channel is over 20 miles wide. Its salt water is cold and rough. Also, the tides and **currents** in the Channel are strong. They can sweep even the best swimmer out to sea.

"I'm going to try again," Trudy told her father, Henry "Pop" Ederle.

"Good," Pop said. "When you make it across, I will buy you your own car."

On August 6, 1926, Gertrude Ederle stood again on the French side of the English Channel. She wore a pair of goggles. She was covered with three coats of grease to keep her body from losing heat. At 7:09 that morning, she waded into the water at Cape Griz-Nez.

A little way off shore, a tugboat was waiting for Trudy. In it were Bill Burgess, Pop Ederle, and several friends. They planned to stay with her as she made her swim.

For the first three hours, Trudy faced rough waters. Still, she moved quickly. At noon, Burgess hung a baby bottle over the side of the boat. It contained clear chicken soup. He also dropped Trudy a chicken leg. She ate, then kept swimming.

That afternoon the wind kicked up. The water became rougher. Trudy slowed down a bit. But then she reached the halfway point. She heard her friends singing "The Star-Spangled Banner." Trudy felt a new rush of energy. She even began to sing along with them.

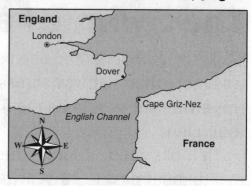

At 3:50 P.M. she called to Burgess. "How much longer before I reach England?"

"About five hours," he answered.

"Don't forget that car, Trudy!" Pop shouted out.

"I won't!" she called back. "I'll be driving it in just a few days!"

Over the next three hours, the storm grew worse. Rain poured down. The wind howled. The waves became stronger. At 6:05 P.M. Burgess shook his head. "We've got to get her out," he said to Pop. "No one can keep swimming in this weather."

"Come out!" he yelled to Trudy.

"What for?" Trudy called. Her tongue was **swollen** from the salt water. Her whole body was **battered** from the rough seas. But her body and her spirit were still strong.

At 7:35 P.M. she finally reached the in-shore tide. The waves were now helping to sweep her toward shore. At 9:30 P.M. she saw lights on the beaches of England. Thousands of people clapped and cheered as Trudy swam toward them. Five minutes later, she reached the shore of Dover, England. She had done it! She had crossed the English Channel. In doing so, Trudy had swum 35 miles. And she had beaten the world's record for the crossing by over two hours.

⬤━━▶ Do you remember the sequence of events? Write **1** before the sentence that tells what happened first in the story. Write **2** before the sentence that tells what happened next, and so on.

_____ Burgess told Trudy to come out of the water.

_____ Trudy reached the shore of Dover, England.

_____ Trudy heard her friends singing "The Star-Spangled Banner."

_____ Burgess dropped Trudy a chicken leg.

_____ Trudy waded into the water at Cape Griz-Nez.

Name _____ Date _____

Comprehension and Vocabulary Review

➤ **Darken the circle by the best answer.**

1. The water in the English Channel is ____.
   Ⓐ deep and still
   Ⓑ filled with sharks
   Ⓒ cold and salty
   Ⓓ hot and sandy

2. During her swim, Trudy ate ____.
   Ⓐ fish sticks
   Ⓑ a chicken leg
   Ⓒ a steak sandwich
   Ⓓ nothing

3. To keep her body from losing heat, Trudy was covered with ____.
   Ⓐ grease
   Ⓑ wool
   Ⓒ lotion
   Ⓓ nothing

4. You can conclude from the article that ____.
   Ⓐ Trudy did not like to swim
   Ⓑ Trudy was ready to give up
   Ⓒ Trudy was determined to complete her swim
   Ⓓ Trudy did not want a new car

5. Something that counts for a record is ____.
   Ⓐ official
   Ⓑ currents
   Ⓒ battered
   Ⓓ swollen

6. A synonym for *battered* is ____.
   Ⓐ wet
   Ⓑ long
   Ⓒ beaten
   Ⓓ angry

7. Areas of water in an ocean that move in a certain direction are called ____.
   Ⓐ official
   Ⓑ currents
   Ⓒ battered
   Ⓓ swollen

8. Something that is ____ has become larger than usual.
   Ⓐ official
   Ⓑ currents
   Ⓒ battered
   Ⓓ swollen

Narration of Process

 **BEFORE READING**

Tap Prior Knowledge
"How Far Is the Moon?": Ask the students if they know how far away the Moon is. Poll the class for possible answers.

"How You Hear": Ask the students if they know how they hear sounds. Ask for an explanation; then tell the students that the process is quite complicated.

"The Amazing Monarchs": Ask the students if they have ever seen a monarch butterfly. Ask them if they know about animals that migrate. Ask them if they know how a butterfly changes from a caterpillar into a butterfly.

Skill to Emphasize
Review the section about narration of process on page 41. Tell the students that they will find the sequence, or order, of steps in each article. A process is a way in which something is done, such as baking a cake or hearing a sound.

 **DURING READING**

Preview Text Features
Point out the titles of the first two articles. The titles give the students information about the process they will read about. Point out the numbered steps in "How Far Is the Moon?" Point out the diagram of the ear in "How You Hear." Point out the subheadings and map in "The Amazing Monarchs." Boldfaced words in the articles indicate vocabulary words.

Comprehending the Selection
Model how to identify the sequence by asking: *What words or clues tell you the order of steps in the process?*

 **AFTER READING**

Reinforce the Comprehension Skill
Tell the students that in a narration of process, the sequence will be in chronological order. The steps in a how-to are presented in the order they should be done.

Distribute copies of the Sequence Chart on page 120. Have the students complete the chart for "How You Hear" and "The Amazing Monarchs." They can use another sheet of paper if necessary.

Assess
Have the students complete the activities for the selections.

 **WRITE ABOUT IT**

Have the students write a how-to process about something they know how to do well.

Name _____ Date _____

How Far Is the Moon?

The moon is Earth's satellite. How far away is the Moon? In this how-to activity, you will find the distance between Earth and the Moon.

First, gather the following materials.

Materials:
index card
string 2 m (80 in.) long
tape
metric ruler
scissors

Next, follow these steps.

1. As shown in the picture above, cut a round notch in one edge of the index card. The notch should be exactly 1 cm (2.5 in.) wide.
2. On a night when there is a full Moon, tape the card to a window from which you can see the Moon. Then tape one end of the string to the card.
3. Look at the Moon through the notch in the card. As you hold the end of the string, back up until the Moon fills the notch.
4. Carefully hold the string up to your eye. Have another person measure the length of the string between the notch and your eye.
5. Multiply the length of the string by 3,500 km (2,170 mi.). This will tell you the distance to the Moon.

Finally, answer these questions.

1. What was the length of the string between the notch and your eye? _____

2. What is the distance from Earth to the Moon? _____

Comprehension Review

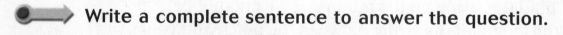

Darken the circle by the best answer.

1. What does this activity tell you how to do?
   Ⓐ find the Moon in the sky
   Ⓑ tell when the Moon is full
   Ⓒ find the distance to the Moon
   Ⓓ take a picture of the Moon

2. How wide should the notch in the card be?
   Ⓐ 1 cm
   Ⓑ 1 in.
   Ⓒ 2 m
   Ⓓ 3,500 km

3. Right after you cut the notch in the card, you should ____.
   Ⓐ look at the Moon through the notch
   Ⓑ tape the card to a window
   Ⓒ hold the string up to your eye
   Ⓓ multiply the length of the string by 3,500 km

4. After you hold the string up to your eye, you should ____.
   Ⓐ tape the card to a window
   Ⓑ tape one end of the string to the card
   Ⓒ have another person measure the string between the notch and your eye
   Ⓓ cut a notch in the card

5. After you measure the string between the notch and your eye, you should ____.
   Ⓐ tape one end of the string to the card
   Ⓑ back up until the Moon fills the notch
   Ⓒ look at the Moon through the notch
   Ⓓ multiply the length of the string by 3,500 km

Write a complete sentence to answer the question.

6. Was the Moon closer or farther from the Earth than you thought it was?

_____

_____

_____

_____

50

How You Hear

You hear many different sounds every day. You hear people talking. You hear music and the sounds of cars. You may have learned that sound is caused by **vibrations**. Vibrations send sound waves through the air. But how do your ears turn these sound waves into the sounds you hear?

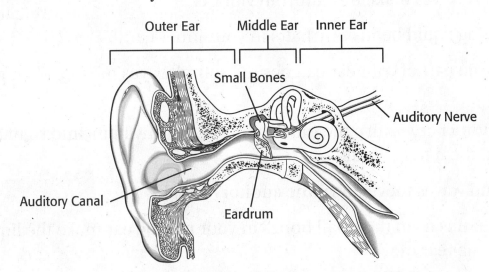

The Parts of the Ear

Your ear has three main parts. They are the outer ear, the middle ear, and the inner ear. The outside part of your ear catches sound waves moving through the air. Then the waves move down the **auditory canal**. You can see the opening of the auditory canal in the middle of your outer ear. The outside part of your ear and the auditory canal are both part of the outer ear.

Sound waves move down the auditory canal to the **eardrum**. The eardrum is a thin piece of skin across the auditory canal. Sound waves make the eardrum vibrate. The vibrations from the eardrum are passed on to three small bones in the middle ear. The bones make the vibrations larger.

The inner ear is filled with liquid. The vibrations from the bones in the middle ear make the liquid move. The moving liquid bends tiny hairs in your inner ear. Your **auditory nerves** feel these hairs move. The auditory nerves turn these movements into signals and send them to the brain. These signals are the sounds you hear.

Sequence and Comprehension Review

➤ **The steps below describe how you hear. Number the steps in the correct order. The first one is done for you.**

____ The sound waves make the eardrum vibrate.

____ The moving liquid bends tiny hairs in your inner ear.

_1_ The outside part of your ear catches the sound waves moving through the air.

____ The auditory nerves turn the movements of the tiny hairs into signals and send them to the brain.

____ The sound waves move down the auditory canal.

____ The vibrations from the small bones in your middle ear make the liquid in your inner ear move.

____ You hear the sound.

➤ **Darken the circle by the best answer.**

1. Your ear has ____ main parts.
   Ⓐ no
   Ⓑ one
   Ⓒ three
   Ⓓ seven

2. This article is mostly about ____.
   Ⓐ music that sounds good
   Ⓑ how you hear sounds
   Ⓒ how the brain works
   Ⓓ sound waves

3. The inner ear is filled with ____.
   Ⓐ liquid
   Ⓑ drums
   Ⓒ air
   Ⓓ brains

4. The auditory nerves send signals to the ____.
   Ⓐ outer ear
   Ⓑ brain
   Ⓒ eardrum
   Ⓓ small bones

The Amazing Monarchs

Have you ever seen or read about butterflies? Have you ever seen them flying in a group? Where did you think they were going? Did you know that monarch butterflies fly south for the winter like some birds do? Monarch butterflies cannot survive the winters of North America. Each fall, millions of monarchs fly south from Canada and parts of the United States. They fly to places in Mexico for the winter. Some monarchs may travel up to 3,000 miles (4,828 kilometers). Then they return home the following spring.

This **migration** happens every year. However, each monarch makes the round trip only once. By the time the migration takes place again the following fall, the monarchs have had many babies. Those new butterflies, in turn, have had babies of their own. It is now a new generation's turn to fly south.

The Journey Begins

Migration begins in late summer and early fall. It begins after each butterfly comes out of its **chrysalis**. Now the butterflies may look like adults, but they are not fully grown. These monarchs will not mate or lay eggs yet. Their bodies must get ready for the journey instead. They eat more so that they can store fat in their bodies. The fat gives them energy for the long flight. It also helps the monarchs survive the winter.

As the monarchs head south, they stop to feed on **nectar**. This gives them more energy. Monarchs are **solitary** creatures by day, but at night they **cluster** in groups.

Nonfiction Comprehension: Grades 3–4, SV 8947-8

Monarchs that migrate to Mexico come from different places. Some come from Canada. Others come from the Midwestern and Eastern United States. All their flight paths lead to the southwest of the United States. Then the monarchs fly to the mountains of central Mexico.

Winter in Mexico

When the monarchs arrive in Mexico, they have finally reached their destination. They cluster together on fir trees along mountain slopes. They cover the trunks and branches and cling to the needles on the trees. It is cool, but not too cold. This is just what monarchs need. When it is cool, they don't use up as much energy as they do in warm weather. They must save their energy for spring.

The trees protect the monarchs from winds, rain, snow, and hail. Fog and clouds also give them the moisture they need. On days when it gets warm enough, the monarchs fly to nearby streams to drink. However, they must return before it gets too cold to fly. Sometimes monarchs fall out of the trees. If it is too cold to fly, they sometimes crawl into bushes. Mexico is the perfect winter **habitat** for the monarchs.

Flight Paths of Monarch Butterflies

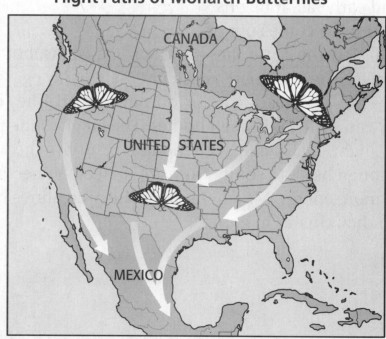

The Return

As winter ends, the monarchs begin to mate. Between the end of February and the beginning of March, they leave Mexico. They fly back north. When they reach the southern United States, the monarchs search for milkweed plants. They lay their eggs there before they die. This begins the next generation of monarchs. Soon a caterpillar hatches from each egg. The caterpillar feeds on milkweed leaves and grows quickly. Then it will **molt** its skin several times. After the last time, it forms a chrysalis. The body of a butterfly then forms inside. Finally, after about fourteen days, an adult butterfly **emerges**.

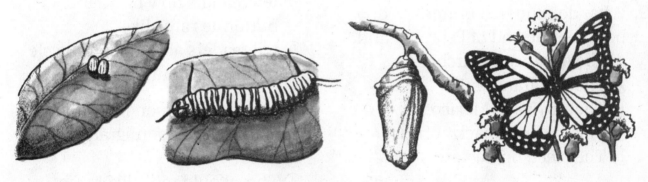

In early summer, some butterflies stay in the southern United States. But many continue north as the weather gets warmer. The monarchs lay more eggs each time they stop. It takes four or five generations of monarchs to reach their destination. Some go back to Canada. Some go to the Midwestern and Eastern United States. By the end of summer, there are millions of monarchs. It is time to migrate south again.

Name _____ Date_____

Comprehension Review

➤ **Darken the circle by the best answer.**

1. Monarch butterflies migrate to Mexico and then return to North America every ____.
   Ⓐ two years
   Ⓑ year
   Ⓒ six months
   Ⓓ week

2. What do monarch butterflies do between the end of February and the beginning of March?
   Ⓐ They migrate south.
   Ⓑ They arrive in Mexico.
   Ⓒ They migrate back north.
   Ⓓ They feed on nectar.

3. The author wrote this article mainly to ____.
   Ⓐ entertain readers with an unbelievable story about monarch butterflies
   Ⓑ ask readers to visit Mexico to observe monarch butterflies
   Ⓒ tell readers how birds and butterflies are alike
   Ⓓ tell readers about the life cycle of monarch butterflies

4. What might happen if monarch butterflies did not migrate to Mexico?
   Ⓐ They would most likely die.
   Ⓑ They would most likely lay more eggs.
   Ⓒ Nothing would happen.
   Ⓓ They would most likely survive.

➤ **Write complete sentences to answer each question. Use your own paper if you need to.**

5. Why is it important for monarchs to return north after the milkweed plants have grown and not before? _____

_____

6. Summarize the process as a butterfly changes from a caterpillar to a butterfly. _____

_____

Vocabulary Review

➤ **Write a vocabulary word from the box to complete each sentence.**

> chrysalis   habitat   migration   molt   nectar   solitary

The field near our house is a great summer _____ for
₁

monarch butterflies because there are milkweed plants. They can also get

_____ from the wildflowers. Last week I saw a large caterpillar
₂

_____ its skin. Then I saw how it had formed a
₃

_____ around itself. It won't be long before it becomes a
₄

butterfly. Monarchs seem to be _____ creatures. I've only seen
₅

one or two in the field at a time. The monarchs will soon begin their fall

_____.
₆

Build Your Vocabulary

Dictionaries give word spellings to help the reader with pronunciations.
They also give definitions of the word.

➤ **Answer the first part of each item by writing a word from the box. Answer the second part by circling the correct definition.**

> emerges   cluster

7. Write the correct spelling of (KLUSS tuhr). _____
   This word means ____.
   A to stand or grow close together   **B** to blow away

8. Write the correct spelling of (ee MUR jez). _____
   This word means ____.
   A comes out   **B** goes inside

Cause-Effect

SELECTION DETAILS

Summary

"Water Changes the Surface" (page 59) tells how moving water causes erosion and weathering.

"Health and Drug Abuse" (page 61) tells the effects of amphetamine and barbiturate use.

"Dogsleds to the Rescue" (page 63) tells how a diphtheria outbreak prompts the courageous acts of mushers and their dog teams.

Selection Type

Science Articles
Social Studies Article

Comprehension Skill

Identify Cause and Effect

Standards

Reading
- Understand cause and effect in a factual article.

Science
- Study the effects of water movement on landforms.
- Study the effects of drug use and abuse on the human body.

Social Studies
- Read a factual account of a heroic effort to transport antitoxin to sick people.

VOCABULARY

Introduce the vocabulary words and write them on the board. Help students find a definition for each word. Have students use each word in a sentence.

"Water Changes the Surface"
weathering   erosion
delta

"Health and Drug Abuse"
illegal   prescribed
barbiturates   overdose
amphetamines

"Dogsleds to the Rescue"
diphtheria   antitoxin
musher   risk
precious

Tap Prior Knowledge

"Water Changes the Surface": Ask the students if they have ever seen rushing water after a storm. Moving water can eat away dirt and even rock, causing erosion and weathering.

"Health and Drug Abuse": Ask the students if they know the difference between legal and illegal drugs. Lead the students to understand that drug abuse can include legal drugs used the wrong way.

"Dogsleds to the Rescue": Ask the students if they know how cold Alaska gets in the winter. Ask the students if they have ever been really sick. What if no one could help them while they were sick? How would they feel?

Skill to Emphasize

Review the section about cause and effect on page 41. Tell the students that many things that happen are caused by other things. What happens is an effect. What caused it to happen is a cause. Sometimes an effect then becomes a cause.

Preview Text Features

Point out the title of the first article. It gives an idea of the cause-effect relationship. Have the students look out for signal words that indicate a cause-effect relationship, such as *because, since, therefore, so, thus,* and *as a result.* Boldfaced words in the articles indicate vocabulary words.

Comprehending the Selection

Model how to identify causes and effects by asking: *What is one thing that happened in the article? What caused that thing to happen?*

Reinforce the Comprehension Skill

Tell the students that in cause-effect relationships, one cause can have many effects, and one effect can have many causes. Students should think about why things happen, then be able to identify the cause of events or the effects of causes.

Distribute copies of the Cause-Effect Chart on page 121. Have the students complete the chart for the articles.

Assess

Have the students complete the activities for the selections.

Have the students write about something that happened to them recently. Have them identify the causes of what happened.

Have the students look for a nursery rhyme or book that has cause-effect situations. Have them bring the nursery rhyme or book to school to share with the class.

Water Changes the Surface

Moving water is the major cause of **weathering** and **erosion** on Earth. Rain, rivers, and ocean waves are examples of moving water.

Rain causes weathering of rocks and soil. Some rocks, like limestone, may break down or dissolve in water. Little by little, rain dissolves the rock and washes it away.

As rain splashes against the ground, it loosens tiny bits of soil. When rain begins to flow across the ground, it is called run-off. Run-off flows from small paths of water down into larger paths of water. The run-off carries the loosened soil into rivers.

Water that flows in rivers wears away the land and moves rocks and soil downhill. Flowing water may wear away the riverbed and make a V-shaped canyon. Flowing water may also cut away the banks of a river. Then the river begins to flow in curves. Often the water in the middle of rivers flows slowly. Slow-flowing water can deposit the rocks and soil it has picked up. These deposits can make a landform like the Mississippi River **delta**.

As a river flows into the ocean, it drops some of the material it is carrying. The water in oceans is always moving. This makes waves that pound against the shore. Waves wear away the land, making steep cliffs. Ocean waves can deposit the sand and soil they are carrying. These deposits can make sandbars near the shore. They also make sandy beaches.

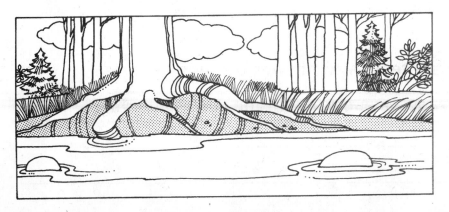

Name _____ Date _____

Comprehension and Vocabulary Review

→ **Darken the circle by the best answer.**

1. Water that flows in rivers moves rocks and soil ____.
   Ⓐ into the sky
   Ⓑ uphill
   Ⓒ downhill
   Ⓓ into a big trash can

2. As rain hits the ground, ____.
   Ⓐ it jumps back into the sky
   Ⓑ the ground gets mad
   Ⓒ it loosens bits of soil
   Ⓓ it turns into rocks

3. This article is mostly about ____.
   Ⓐ how moving water never causes erosion
   Ⓑ how the water in oceans is always moving
   Ⓒ how sandbars form near a shore
   Ⓓ how moving water causes erosion and weathering

4. You can tell from the article that run-off ____.
   Ⓐ dissolves in water
   Ⓑ does not soak into the ground
   Ⓒ is not moving water
   Ⓓ is made of limestone

5. Flowing water may wear away the riverbed and make a ____.
   Ⓐ sandbar
   Ⓑ beach
   Ⓒ V-shaped canyon
   Ⓓ delta

6. Waves wear away the land, ____.
   Ⓐ then build a swimming pool there
   Ⓑ then make steep cliffs
   Ⓒ then cut away the banks of a river
   Ⓓ then form a V-shaped canyon

→ **Write complete sentences to answer the question.**

7. What are two ways moving water causes erosion and weathering?

_____

_____

Lesson 10: Cause and Effect
Nonfiction Comprehension: Grades 3–4, SV 8947-8

Health and Drug Abuse

A drug is a substance other than food that changes the way the body works. You probably know how alcohol changes the way the body works. Alcohol is a drug. Some drugs, like alcohol, are legal. You can buy legal drugs like aspirin in stores. Other drugs are **illegal**. They can be bought only on the street.

Some legal drugs are **prescribed** by doctors. These drugs help sick people get well. But even these drugs can be abused.

Barbiturates are legal drugs. They slow down the nervous system. For this reason, they are known as "downers." Doctors may prescribe barbiturates for people who have trouble sleeping. But taking barbiturates when a doctor has not prescribed them is abusing them. An **overdose**, or taking too much at one time, can kill a person. Mixing barbiturates and alcohol can also lead to death.

Amphetamines are legal drugs that speed up the nervous system. For this reason, they are called "speed" or "uppers." Doctors may prescribe amphetamines for people who need to lose weight. Other people take the drug for the excited feeling it gives them. As the drug wears off, the drug user feels bad and wants more to feel better.

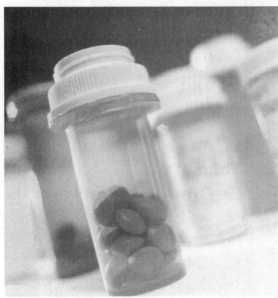

Even legal drugs should not be taken without a doctor's prescription.

Barbiturates and amphetamines change the speed of the heartbeat. When these drugs are abused, they can cause heart failure.

Comprehension Review

 Darken the circle by the best answer.

1. Drugs that doctors tell people to take are ____.
   Ⓐ illegal
   Ⓑ free
   Ⓒ prescribed
   Ⓓ food

2. Using a drug the wrong way or using too much of it is ____ the drug.
   Ⓐ prescribing
   Ⓑ abusing
   Ⓒ buying
   Ⓓ losing

3. When barbiturates and amphetamines are abused, they can cause ____.
   Ⓐ heart failure
   Ⓑ hunger
   Ⓒ food
   Ⓓ foot problems

4. Barbiturates are also called ____.
   Ⓐ uppers
   Ⓑ alcohol
   Ⓒ speed
   Ⓓ downers

 Draw lines between the words and the effects they cause.

5. drug   speed up the nervous system

6. barbiturates   too much of a drug or drugs at one time

7. overdose   slow down the nervous system

8. amphetamines   changes the way the body works

Nonfiction Comprehension: Grades 3–4, SV 8947-8

Dogsleds to the Rescue

Dr. Curtis Welch stared at the sick young boy. He had a fever, and his throat was swollen. Every few minutes he broke into a deep cough. Dr. Welch shook his head and muttered, "**Diphtheria**. He and many others will die if we don't get medicine soon. Diphtheria spreads very quickly."

Dr. Welch was worried. Most people who came down with diphtheria died. There was a cure—a medicine called **antitoxin**. But Welch didn't have any. There wasn't any for miles around. He feared the disease would kill everyone in the frozen town of Nome, Alaska.

The next day, January 27, 1925, Dr. Welch sent a message to other Alaskan cities. He needed antitoxin fast. The nearest antitoxin was in Anchorage, about 900 miles away. All the roads were closed for the winter. Planes couldn't fly because of the winds and cold. The railroad tracks only came as far as Nenana, which was over 650 miles from Nome.

The governor of Alaska decided the antitoxin should be sent by railroad from Anchorage to Nenana. From there, it would be carried by relay teams of dogsleds. A **musher** and his dogs would take the antitoxin from Nenana to the next town. The next musher would then take the antitoxin. It would change hands about 20 times before it reached Nome. The plan had to be carried out quickly, or it would be too late.

The trip would be difficult. The mushers and their dogs would face temperatures of 50 degrees below zero, howling winds, and blinding snow. Some of the dogs might not make it. Some of the mushers might not either. Many mushers quickly stepped forward to do the job. They knew it was dangerous. But they knew how to handle their dogs. They knew the way. The mushers were willing to **risk** their lives to help the people of Nome.

Nonfiction Comprehension: Grades 3–4, SV 8947-8

One by one, the mushers carried the antitoxin west toward Nome. All of Alaska watched and waited during this race against time and the weather. On February 1, the antitoxin reached a small village. It was still over 150 miles from Nome. Here musher Leonard Seppala made a bold decision.

"I'm not going to follow the trail up around Norton Bay," he said. "I'm going to take the shortcut straight across the frozen water."

"In this storm?" one of the townspeople asked. "Those 80-mile-per-hour winds will break up the ice. You and your dogs will fall in and be swallowed up by the water."

But Seppala knew that if he made it, he would save **precious** hours. All around him the snow blew in angry clouds. His dogs slipped on the ice. They groaned. They whimpered. Still he drove them on. At last, he reached the other side of the bay.

Gunnar Kasson was the last musher. He had to travel 60 miles to reach Nome. It was 8:00 P.M., and the sky was black. He couldn't wait for morning. He knew that five people had already died. At least 30 more people had caught the disease.

Kasson called to Balto, his lead dog. Balto guided the sled to the snowy trail. Soon the wind grew worse. The freezing air cut through Kasson's heavy winter clothes. It froze his right cheek. His hands ached. The dogs were in pain, too. Pieces of ice stuck in their feet. Their paws began to bleed.

And then Kasson lost the trail. The swirling snow had swept away his sense of direction. He prayed that Balto could pick up the scent of the trail again. If not, all was lost. Balto sniffed around in the snow. He turned one way, then another. Soon, Balto picked up speed. He had found the trail!

At 5:36 the next morning, Kasson and his dogs limped into Nome. Kasson collapsed in the snow next to his half-frozen dogs.

"Fine dog," he mumbled again and again. "Balto, you brought us through. You brought us through."

People cheered all the dogs who had made the trip. Kasson and Seppala and the other mushers were heroes. These brave people and their animals had saved the lives of many Alaskans.

Comprehension Review

➡ **Darken the circle by the best answer.**

1. Dr. Welch was treating a boy who had ____.
   Ⓐ measles
   Ⓑ chicken pox
   Ⓒ diphtheria
   Ⓓ earaches

2. A cure for diphtheria was a medicine called ____.
   Ⓐ anteater
   Ⓑ anthill
   Ⓒ shortcut
   Ⓓ antitoxin

3. The nearest medicine was in ____.
   Ⓐ Nome
   Ⓑ Anchorage
   Ⓒ Montana
   Ⓓ Nenana

4. The last lead dog was named ____.
   Ⓐ Balto
   Ⓑ Welch
   Ⓒ Kasson
   Ⓓ Seppala

➡ **Write a conclusion to finish each sentence.**

5. When Dr. Welch saw that the child had diphtheria, he was very worried because

_____

_____.

6. Planes couldn't fly at this time because

_____

_____.

7. Seppala decided to take the shortcut across frozen water because

_____

_____.

8. The dogs' paws began to bleed because

_____

_____.

Nonfiction Comprehension: Grades 3–4, SV 8947-8

Vocabulary Review

→ Darken the circle by the best answer.

1. The word *fever* means ____.
   Ⓐ high body temperature
   Ⓑ pain
   Ⓒ not as many
   Ⓓ cure

2. A synonym for *disease* is ____.
   Ⓐ medicine
   Ⓑ cure
   Ⓒ sickness
   Ⓓ dangerous

3. Diphtheria is a ____.
   Ⓐ cure
   Ⓑ relay
   Ⓒ antitoxin
   Ⓓ disease

4. A relay ____.
   Ⓐ uses a series of teams to complete a race
   Ⓑ is made of snow and ice
   Ⓒ is a kind of disease
   Ⓓ is a cure for diphtheria

5. The word *musher* means ____.
   Ⓐ a meal
   Ⓑ a police officer
   Ⓒ a kind of sled
   Ⓓ a dogsled driver

6. Something that is precious is ____.
   Ⓐ not worth much
   Ⓑ valuable and important
   Ⓒ short
   Ⓓ dangerous

7. The word *risk* means ____.
   Ⓐ tear apart
   Ⓑ remove
   Ⓒ take a chance
   Ⓓ rent

8. The word *collapsed* means ____.
   Ⓐ fell down
   Ⓑ jumped up and down
   Ⓒ waited
   Ⓓ relaxed

Nonfiction Comprehension: Grades 3–4, SV 8947-8

Description is concerned with the relationship between the whole and its parts. It can be used to provide physical description, in which details of a person, place, or object are presented to appeal to the reader's senses. It also can be used for division, to identify the component parts that make up the whole of something. In both these forms, the function of description is to demonstrate how the parts work together to produce the whole.

Physical Description— Unique Details (Lesson 11)

Students use physical description on a daily basis to characterize the things around them. They might say, "I ate a juicy orange for lunch" or "The cold ice cream made my tongue tingle" or "We got a new blue car." Each of these descriptions gives physical details about an object. By using these physical details, the writer appeals to the reader's senses. The more of the reader's senses that are brought into play, the more effective is the physical description.

A good physical description will downplay the common features to show the uniqueness of the subject. An assumption is made that all people have two arms or two ears or a nose. Lack of these things would be a kind of uniqueness, or unusual features, such as a long nose, would also be a sign of uniqueness. The details that distinguish one person from another, for example, are the unique features, not the common ones. By showing both common and unique features, description becomes very important in mastering the later skill of classification.

The more thorough the description, the more effectively a sense of the whole is achieved. If a writer says a room has a door and two windows, the reader gets a rough sense of the thing being described. By adding details about the parts, the sense of the whole is more completely realized. As the writer provides more details and a more effective whole, the reader more easily experiences the thing being described.

Research Base

"Content literacy involves the strategies required to read, comprehend, and write informational texts in a variety of subjects. Different styles and ways of organizing texts are used for different subjects." (*Guiding Readers and Writers: Grades 3–6*, p. 400)

To get the most information from a physical description:

- First, identify the thing being described (for example, a building).
- Look for details about parts of the thing (for example, doors, windows, walls, roof).
- Look for words that appeal to the senses of sight, smell, taste, touch, and hearing.
- Put all the details together to get the whole picture.
- Try to draw a picture of the thing on paper or in your mind.
- Decide how the thing described is unique or different from other things.
- Try to write a summary description of the thing.

Physical Description— Parts, or Division (Lesson 12)

Like physical description, division is a form of organization that shows how the various parts make up the whole. Division is not the same as classification. Division shows the parts of the whole, whereas classification puts things into different groups. Classification would put the school building into *kinds* of buildings, but division would discuss the *parts* of the school building.

Physical description is often a part of division. The parts of the whole are described. However, the main focus of division is to identify the parts that are used to create the whole. You might ask the students, "What are the parts of the classroom?" or "What are the parts of a book?" Using the organizational skill of division, the students can more easily see how the parts work together to create the object.

To get the most information from an article of division:

- First, identify the topic being discussed (for example, the parts of a plant).
- Look for descriptive details about the parts (for example, stem, petals, leaves).
- Pay attention to what each part does in relation to the whole (for example, the stem holds up the plant).
- Put all the parts together to produce the whole thing.
- Try to draw a picture of the thing on paper or in your mind.
- Highlight each part in your picture.
- Try to write a summary that tells how the parts work together to make up the whole thing.

Physical Description—Unique Details

SELECTION DETAILS

Summary
"Starfish" (page 69) describes the appearance and behavior of starfish.

"Plants That Attract Insects" (page 71) describes the adaptations of flowers that allow them to attract insects.

"Chief Joseph" (page 73) describes the capture of Chief Joseph and his speech after his capture.

Selection Type
Science Articles
Social Studies Article

Comprehension Skill
Identify Sensory Words in Descriptive Article

Standards
Reading
- Identify words that appeal to the senses.
- Identify details in a reading selection.

Science
- Learn about the characteristics and behavior of plants and animals.

Social Studies
- Read a factual account of a historical person.

VOCABULARY

Introduce the vocabulary words and write them on the board. Help students find a definition for each word. Have students use each word in a sentence.

"Starfish"
invertebrates	spines
tube	suction
mollusks	

"Plants That Attract Insects"
reproduce	pollination
adaptations	pistil

"Chief Joseph"
reservations

 **BEFORE READING**

Tap Prior Knowledge
"Starfish": Have the students draw a starfish. Then point out that a starfish is not really a fish, but it is an invertebrate.

"Plants That Attract Insects": Ask the students if they have ever seen a bee flying around from flower to flower. Ask the students for suggestions about what the bee was doing.

"Chief Joseph": Ask the students what they would do if their family was told they had to move to a certain place. How would they feel?

Skill to Emphasize
Review the section about physical description on page 67. Tell the students that good writers use words that appeal to the reader's senses of sight, smell, taste, touch, and hearing. Sensory words make the writing more interesting and vivid.

 **DURING READING**

Preview Text Features
Point out the title of each article. The titles give the students information about the things that will be described. Have the students look at the illustrations to get a better idea of what is being described. Boldfaced words indicate vocabulary words.

Comprehending the Selection
Model a better understanding of physical description by asking: *What words in the article appeal to your senses of sight, smell, taste, touch, and hearing?*

 **AFTER READING**

Reinforce the Comprehension Skill
Tell the students that a good description helps them to see an object clearly in their mind. Ask the students to point out words in "Starfish" and "Plants That Attract Insects" that allow them to see the starfish or plant clearly in their mind. What picture can they see in their mind after reading the article about Chief Joseph, especially his speech?

Assess
Have the students complete the activities for the selections.

 **WRITE ABOUT IT**

Have the students write a description about a person, place, or thing that they like. Tell them to be sure to use sensory words.

 **AT HOME**

Have students look in the newspaper or magazines for articles that contain descriptions and bring the articles to school to share with the class.

Starfish

Starfish live in all oceans. *Fish* is part of their name, but they are not fish. They are **invertebrates**, which means they do not have backbones. Starfish have a small central body, with a mouth on the bottom side. Most starfish have five arms that stick out from their bodies. Other kinds have more than 25 arms. Stiff **spines** cover their bodies and arms. Starfish are often dull yellow or orange but can be bright colors, too. They can be as small as $\frac{1}{2}$ inch and as big as 3 feet wide.

Starfish use their **tube** feet to move. These small tube feet are under each arm. **Suction** cups are attached to the feet. The suction cups help starfish to move.

Starfish eat animals. Starfish eat **mollusks** like clams and oysters that are valuable crops for the fishing industry. A starfish catches a clam with its arms. The clam closes its shell to protect itself. Using its tube feet, the starfish forces the shell open a little bit. Then the starfish turns its stomach inside out and pushes it out of its mouth. It sticks its stomach into the opened clamshell and eats the soft clam body. Then the starfish pulls its stomach out of the clam and puts it back into its own body.

A starfish can grow new arms if its arms are broken off. In fact, if a starfish loses all its arms but one and most of its central body, a new body and new arms will grow. People may try to destroy starfish by cutting them into pieces. But the pieces grow into even more starfish.

Comprehension and Vocabulary Review

Darken the circle by the best answer.

1. Starfish like to eat _____.
   Ⓐ spines
   Ⓑ other starfish
   Ⓒ clams and other mollusks
   Ⓓ people

2. After the starfish opens the clam shell, it _____.
   Ⓐ knocks the clam out of the shell
   Ⓑ turns its stomach inside out
   Ⓒ is not hungry anymore
   Ⓓ grows a new arm

3. Invertebrates do not have _____.
   Ⓐ feet
   Ⓑ arms
   Ⓒ stomachs
   Ⓓ backbones

4. Most starfish have _____.
   Ⓐ two heads
   Ⓑ five arms
   Ⓒ four legs
   Ⓓ a big nose

5. A tube is shaped like a _____.
   Ⓐ square
   Ⓑ drinking straw
   Ⓒ triangle
   Ⓓ fork

6. The starfish's suction cups help it _____.
   Ⓐ cling to rocks
   Ⓑ open claws
   Ⓒ grow more arms
   Ⓓ float in the water

Write complete sentences to describe a starfish.

_____

_____

_____

_____

_____

Plants That Attract Insects

Most plants **reproduce** from seeds. Seeds are made in flowers. Before seeds can form, a flower must be pollinated. In many plants, insects help **pollination** take place. These plants have **adaptations** that attract insects.

Some flowers have marks on their petals. These marks guide an insect inside the flower. The insect gets nectar from inside the flower and uses the nectar for food. The flower, in turn, gets pollinated as the insect moves around inside the flower.

The colors and smells of flowers attract insects, too. Blue, purple, and yellow flowers attract honeybees. Bees and other insects are also attracted to sweet-smelling flowers like roses and honeysuckle. Some flowers bloom at night. These flowers are often white and have a sweet, spicy smell. Moths that fly at night pollinate these flowers.

The shape of a flower is another adaptation that helps pollination take place. Some flowers have large petals that act like landing platforms for bees. The **pistil**, or female part of the flower, may be just above the platform. As a bee lands, it touches the pistil. Any pollen on the bee gets on the pistil. Then the flower is pollinated.

Some orchids have flowers shaped like female wasps. A male wasp is attracted to the flower and tries to mate with it. The wasp gets pollen on its body. It carries the pollen to the next orchid it visits.

The foxglove flowers have marks that guide insects inside the flower.

Roses have sweet smells.

Comprehension and Vocabulary Review

→ **Darken the circle by the best answer.**

1. *Reproduce* means to _____.
   - Ⓐ bloom at night
   - Ⓑ make others of the same kind
   - Ⓒ take back
   - Ⓓ paint with bright colors

2. Most plants reproduce from _____.
   - Ⓐ leaves
   - Ⓑ nectar
   - Ⓒ seeds
   - Ⓓ moths

3. Before seeds can form, _____.
   - Ⓐ a snowstorm must happen
   - Ⓑ a dog must walk by
   - Ⓒ the flower must turn purple
   - Ⓓ the flower must be pollinated

4. The main idea of this article is that _____.
   - Ⓐ many plants have adaptations that attract insects
   - Ⓑ some flowers have marks on their petals
   - Ⓒ the colors and smells of flowers attract insects
   - Ⓓ some orchids are shaped like female wasps

5. You can conclude from the article that _____.
   - Ⓐ insects cause problems for plants
   - Ⓑ plants and insects are important to each other
   - Ⓒ male wasps are not very smart
   - Ⓓ all flowers bloom at night

6. Pollination is _____.
   - Ⓐ dirt in the air and water
   - Ⓑ the color and smell of flowers
   - Ⓒ the spreading of pollen between plants
   - Ⓓ the female part of a plant

7. An adaptation is _____.
   - Ⓐ a kind of seed
   - Ⓑ a kind of flower
   - Ⓒ a special change in a plant or an animal
   - Ⓓ a kind of bee

8. The female part of a plant is called the _____.
   - Ⓐ nectar
   - Ⓑ honeysuckle
   - Ⓒ pollination
   - Ⓓ pistil

Nonfiction Comprehension: Grades 3–4, SV 8947-8

Chief Joseph

During the 1800s, many American Indians lost their homes. Over and over, the United States government forced American Indians to give their lands to settlers and move to **reservations**. One group that lost their land was the Nez Perce. Their land was in the states of Idaho, Oregon, and Washington.

In the 1870s, some settlers wanted the rich lands for farms. The United States government ordered the Nez Perce to leave their villages. The government wanted them to go to a small reservation in Idaho. The Nez Perce were led by a great chief named Joseph. He tried to get the United States government to let the Nez Perce stay. Then fighting started.

Chief Joseph tried to lead his group to safety in Canada. His people walked 1,600 miles and fought many battles all winter. They were finally caught by the United States Army near Canada. The Nez Perce were taken to Oklahoma, not Idaho.

When he was captured on October 5, 1877, Chief Joseph made a speech. He said, "It is cold and we have no blankets. The little children are freezing to death. My people, some of them, have run away to the hills and have no blankets, no food. No one knows where they are, perhaps freezing to death. I want time to look for my children and see how many of them I can find. Maybe I shall find them among the dead. Hear me, my chiefs, I am tired, my heart is sick and sad. From where the sun now stands, I will fight no more forever."

Comprehension and Vocabulary Review

 Darken the circle by the best answer.

1. What was the weather like when Chief Joseph made his speech?
   - Ⓐ hot
   - Ⓑ windy
   - Ⓒ cold
   - Ⓓ rainy

2. After fighting started, Chief Joseph tried to lead his people to _____.
   - Ⓐ Canada
   - Ⓑ Idaho
   - Ⓒ Oklahoma
   - Ⓓ Nez Perce

3. What did Chief Joseph say was wrong with the little children?
   - Ⓐ They had nowhere to play.
   - Ⓑ They did not want to go to Canada.
   - Ⓒ They had no hats.
   - Ⓓ They were freezing to death.

4. The main idea of Chief Joseph's speech is that _____.
   - Ⓐ Canada is too cold
   - Ⓑ his people need blankets
   - Ⓒ he will fight no more
   - Ⓓ his chiefs can't hear well

5. In his speech, how does Chief Joseph describe his heart?
   - Ⓐ It is happy.
   - Ⓑ It is sick and sad.
   - Ⓒ It is full of love.
   - Ⓓ It is freezing

6. A reservation is an area set aside for the American Indians. Where was the reservation the government wanted the Nez Perce group to go at first?
   - Ⓐ Idaho
   - Ⓑ Oklahoma
   - Ⓒ Canada
   - Ⓓ Oregon

 Write complete sentences to answer the question.

7. What did Chief Joseph say he wanted time to do?

_____

_____

_____

LESSON 12

Physical Description– Parts, or Division

Summary
"The Parts of a Tree" (page 76) identifies and describes the parts of a tree.

"The Structure of Earth" (page 79) identifies and describes the four layers of Earth.

Selection Type
Science Articles

Comprehension Skill
Identify Important Details in a Division Article

Standards
Reading
- Identify component parts of a whole.
- Identify details in a reading selection.

Science
- Learn about the parts of a tree.
- Learn about the four layers of Earth.

VOCABULARY

Introduce the vocabulary words and write them on the board. Help students find a definition for each word. Have students use each word in a sentence.

"The Parts of a Tree"

taproot	fibrous roots
trunk	bark
sapwood	sap
inner bark	heartwood

"The Structure of Earth"

inner core	outer core
mantle	crust

BEFORE READING

Tap Prior Knowledge
"The Parts of a Tree": Ask the students to name and describe all the parts of a tree they can think of. Likely they will know the roots, bark, leaves, and trunk of the tree. Tell them that the tree also contains parts they cannot see.

"The Structure of Earth": Ask the students how many layers Earth has. Ask them which layer of Earth they live on. Point out that there are four layers of Earth, and the article will give details about each.

Skill to Emphasize
Review the section about division on page 67. Tell the students that division is a kind of writing that tells about the parts of something. A good division article helps the students to see more easily how the parts work together to make up the object.

DURING READING

Preview Text Features
Point out the title of each article. The titles give the students information about the things that will be divided. Have the students look at the illustrations. The illustrations show the parts that make up the whole. Boldfaced words indicate vocabulary words.

Comprehending the Selection
Model a better understanding of division by asking: *What are the parts that make up the whole?*

AFTER READING

Reinforce the Comprehension Skill
Tell the students that a good division article helps them to see how the parts of an object go together to form the whole object. Each part is important and necessary to make the whole. Without roots, for example, a tree could not live.

Assess
Have the students complete the activities for the selections.

WRITE ABOUT IT

Have the students write about something they know that has several parts. Have them identify the whole object, then identify and describe the parts that make up the whole.

AT HOME

Have the students look for instruction manuals that show all the parts of a machine. Have them bring the manuals to school to share with the class.

The Parts of a Tree

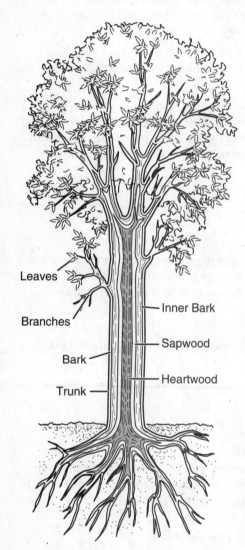

Leaves

Branches

Bark

Trunk

Inner Bark

Sapwood

Heartwood

In most ways, trees are like all other green plants. Like other plants, trees have roots, stems, and leaves. But trees are much larger than other plants. Most trees grow 15 to 20 feet tall. There are even trees as tall as 30-story buildings.

A tree's roots take in water and minerals from the soil. Roots also help hold a tree in place. Some trees have one main root called a **taproot**. The taproot grows straight down in the soil. Other trees have **fibrous roots**. Fibrous roots are a system of roots that spread out in the soil.

The hard, woody stem of a tree is called a **trunk**. The trunk is made up of several layers. There is a tough outside layer called **bark**. Bark protects the tree against insects and diseases. It also protects a tree from too much heat or cold. Under the bark is **sapwood**. Sapwood is full of tubes that carry water and minerals from the roots of the tree to the leaves. This mixture of water and minerals is called **sap**.

Between the sapwood and the bark is the **inner bark**. Food that is made in the leaves is carried to other parts of the tree through the inner bark. The center of the trunk is **heartwood**, the oldest, darkest, and hardest wood in the tree. The heartwood helps support the tree.

The leaves of a tree grow from the branches. The branches hold the leaves up to the light. In sunlight, leaves make all of the food for the tree.

Comprehension Review

➡ **Darken the circle by the best answer.**

1. Most trees grow _____.
   Ⓐ sideways
   Ⓑ 15 to 20 feet tall
   Ⓒ as tall as a 30-story building
   Ⓓ a mile high

4. The stem of a tree is called the _____.
   Ⓐ sap
   Ⓑ branch
   Ⓒ trunk
   Ⓓ taproot

2. Between the bark and the sapwood is the _____.
   Ⓐ taproot
   Ⓑ branches
   Ⓒ inner bark
   Ⓓ heartwood

5. You can conclude from the article that the taproot and the fibrous roots _____.
   Ⓐ grow the same way
   Ⓑ grow differently
   Ⓒ make food for the tree
   Ⓓ are covered with leaves

3. This article is mostly about _____.
   Ⓐ how leaves make food for trees
   Ⓑ how tall trees grow
   Ⓒ what heartwood is
   Ⓓ the different parts of a tree

6. Tubes that carry water are in the _____.
   Ⓐ sapwood
   Ⓑ heartwood
   Ⓒ bark
   Ⓓ inner bark

➡ **Write complete sentences to answer the question.**

7. What is the job of the leaves of a tree?

   _____

   _____

   _____

Vocabulary Review

 Draw a line from the part of the tree to the words that describe it.

1. taproot   hard, woody stem of a tree

2. fibrous roots   mixture of water and minerals in a tree

3. trunk   system of roots that spread out

4. bark   oldest and hardest wood in the tree

5. sapwood   grows straight down into the soil

6. sap   grows between the bark and the sapwood

7. inner bark   full of tubes that carry water and minerals

8. heartwood   tough outside layer of a tree

 Use each word to write a sentence about trees.

9. branches

_____

_____

10. leaves

_____

_____

   Nonfiction Comprehension: Grades 3–4, SV 8947-8

The Structure of Earth

Earth is shaped like a ball and is made up of four layers: the inner core, the outer core, the mantle, and the crust. It is about 8,000 miles in diameter.

At the very center of Earth is the **inner core**. It is about 800 miles thick and is made of the metals iron and nickel. The inner core is very hot, about 9,000° F. Although it is hot enough to melt, the inner core is solid because it is under so much pressure from the layers above. The molecules of iron and nickel cannot spread out enough to become liquid.

The **outer core** is about 1,400 miles thick. It is also made of iron and nickel. The temperature of the outer core ranges from 4,000° F to 9,000° F. Because the outer core is not under as much pressure as the inner core, the iron and nickel have melted. The outer core is made of hot liquid metal.

The **mantle** is the thickest layer of Earth. It is about 1,800 miles thick and lies just below Earth's crust. The mantle seems to be made up of several layers. The top layer of the mantle is hot solid rock. The bottom layer is liquid rock. The rocks in the mantle are made mostly of silicon, aluminum, iron, and magnesium.

The **crust** is the outer layer of Earth. It is about 20 miles thick in most places. But it can be as little as 5 miles thick. The crust makes up the continents and ocean floors. It is made up of many kinds of rock, such as granite, sandstone, and marble.

The outer core is liquid and is about 1,400 miles thick.

The inner core is solid and is about 800 miles thick.

The mantle is the thickest layer. It is 1,800 miles thick.

The crust is the thin outer layer of Earth.

Comprehension Review

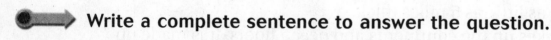 **Darken the circle by the best answer.**

1. The _____ of Earth is made up of many kinds of rock, such as granite, sandstone, and marble.
Ⓐ inner core
Ⓑ outer core
Ⓒ mantle
Ⓓ crust

2. At the very center of Earth is the _____.
Ⓐ inner core
Ⓑ outer core
Ⓒ mantle
Ⓓ crust

3. This article is mostly about _____.
Ⓐ how hot the inner core is
Ⓑ how thick the crust is
Ⓒ what the outer core is made of
Ⓓ the layers of Earth

4. You can conclude from the article that the inside of Earth is _____.
Ⓐ very cold
Ⓑ very hot
Ⓒ full of water
Ⓓ made of air

5. The _____ is the outer layer of Earth.
Ⓐ inner core
Ⓑ outer core
Ⓒ mantle
Ⓓ crust

6. The inner core is _____ rock because it is under so much pressure from the layers above.
Ⓐ melted
Ⓑ solid
Ⓒ gaseous
Ⓓ paper

Write a complete sentence to answer the question.

7. On which of the four parts of Earth do you live?

_____

_____

Name _____   Date_____

Vocabulary Review

➡️ Draw a line from each part of Earth to the words that describe it.

1. inner core   is hot liquid metal

2. outer core   makes up continents and ocean floors

3. mantle   at the very center of Earth

4. crust   the thickest layer

➡️ **Write a complete sentence to describe each part of Earth.**

5. inner core

_____

_____

6. outer core

_____

_____

7. mantle

_____

_____

8. crust

_____

_____

UNIT 5 Classification

Classification is concerned with the relationship between a thing and others of its kind. Formal classification is used to classify things, or to place them in groups. This grouping is based on similarities of the things being grouped. Comparison-contrast is used to show the similarities and differences between two things. In both these forms, classification is used to show how one thing is related to other similar things. The details of similarity and contrast are provided by description.

Classification (Lesson 13)

Students are involved with classification on a daily basis. They are grouped according to their gender and their school grade. They study groups of subjects in school and play different kinds of sports. Classification is a skill that students learn early in their school life. They may be asked to group shapes according to color or size or to identify their favorite food or color.

The process of classification moves from general to specific. A tree diagram is helpful for illustrating this concept; one is provided on page 122. The first level of classification is a very general group, such as Fruits. The next level of classification is more specific. The names of specific fruits are added to the diagram, such as apples, oranges, bananas, and grapes. Then, very specific descriptive details about each fruit are added to the diagram. These details can be used later for comparison-contrast of two fruits.

A tree diagram can have many levels, depending on the needs of the classification. For example, the classification of Fruits could add extra levels. Instead of naming only fruits under the general heading, one could add extra subheadings of kinds of fruits, such as Citrus Fruits and Tropical Fruits. Then, specific fruits could be added to these subheadings, and specific details could be provided for each fruit.

To identify the groups in a classification:

- Use the Classification Tree Diagram on page 122.
- First identify the general group (for example, kinds of pets).
- Then identify any subgroups under the general group (for example, kinds of dogs).
- Then identify the specific members of the general group or subgroup.
- Identify the specific details about each member.
- Think about why the specific members belong in the general group.

Comparison-Contrast (Lesson 14)

Students can easily relate to the concept of comparison-contrast by introducing it using the terms *alike* and *different*. How are two games alike? How are they different? However, comparison-contrast works well only if the two items are from a common category. For example, comparing and contrasting two kinds of food is logical. Comparing and contrasting a banana and a brick is not really logical.

Comparison-contrast is used to show the similarities and differences between things. *Compare* means to show how things are alike. *Contrast* means to show how things are different. If possible, a comparison-contrast should be limited to two items. Three points of comparison-contrast should be used. For example, two people could be compared and contrasted based on their height, hair or eye color, and shoe size. The details about group members in a Tree Diagram are useful in comparing and contrasting.

A Venn Diagram is a useful tool for comparing and contrasting. A Venn Diagram is provided on page 123. The Venn Diagram graphically represents the similarities and differences. The differences are placed in the outer parts of the ovals. The similarities are placed where the two ovals intersect. You might want to distribute a Venn Diagram and allow the students to perform a comparison-contrast before reading the selections. A simple comparison-contrast of apples and oranges would be a good starting point.

To get the most information from a comparison-contrast:

- Use the Venn Diagram on page 123.
- First identify the two things being compared and contrasted.
- Then identify the points used to compare and contrast the two things.
- Think about the ways the things are alike and different.
- Often, the writer is trying to show that one thing is better than another. So be aware of any attempt to persuade the reader.

Graphic Organizers

Classification Tree Diagram	page 122
Venn Diagram	page 123

Nonfiction Comprehension: Grades 3–4, SV 8947-8

Classification

Summary

"Climate Zones" (page 84) classifies the three main climate zones on Earth.

"Types of Sharks" (page 87) classifies several kinds of sharks.

Selection Type

Science Articles

Comprehension Skill

Identify Classification in a Nonfiction Article

Standards

Reading

- Use reading strategies (classification) to comprehend text.
- Organize information logically.
- Identify details in a reading selection.

Science

- Explore the three climate zones of Earth.
- Learn about various kinds of sharks.

Introduce the vocabulary words and write them on the board. Help students find a definition for each word. Have students use each word in a sentence.

"Climate Zones"

climate	tropical
temperate	polar
latitude	equator

"Types of Sharks"

plankton	unusual
schools	

BEFORE READING

Tap Prior Knowledge

"Climate Zones": Ask the students what kind of weather is occurring today. Ask them what kind of weather usually occurs at this time of year. The long-term weather pattern is called climate. Earth has three main climate zones.

"Types of Sharks": Ask the students if they have seen the movie *Jaws*. What kind of shark is in that movie? (great white) Have students draw pictures and describe different kinds of sharks.

Skill to Emphasize

Review the section about classification on page 82. Tell the students that writers often put things in groups to help the reader to identify them more easily.

 DURING READING

Preview Text Features

Have the students look at the map in the "Climate Zones" article. It gives the location of each of the three types of climate zones. The illustrations in the "Types of Sharks" article help the students to envision kinds of sharks. Boldfaced words indicate vocabulary words.

Comprehending the Selection

Model a better understanding of classification by asking: *What general group of things is being discussed? What are the individual members of that group?*

 AFTER READING

Reinforce the Comprehension Skill

Tell the students that a good classification helps them to understand the common features between groups of things. Ask the students to point out the members of each group named in the title of the article. Distribute copies of the Classification Tree Diagram on page 122 to help the students organize the information.

Assess

Have the students complete the activities for the selections.

 WRITE ABOUT IT

Distribute copies of the Classification Tree Diagram on page 122. Have the students choose a general group to classify. Have them include at least three individual members of that group. They should also include details about each individual member. Then, have them write a short classification essay using the information they have compiled in their tree diagram.

 AT HOME

Have students look in the newspaper or magazines for articles that contain classification. Have them bring the articles to school to share with the class.

Climate Zones

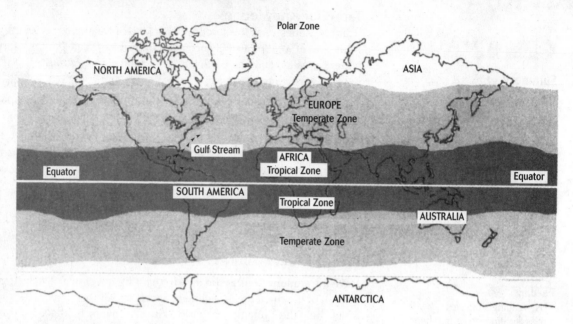

The weather in any one place can change from day to day. But the **climate** of a region does not change very much. Climate is the average weather of a region over a long period of time.

There are three main climate zones: tropical, temperate, and polar. In a **tropical** climate, it is warm all year round and rainfall is high. In a **temperate** climate, winters are cold and summers are warm. There is a moderate amount of rain. In a **polar** climate, it is cold much of the year, and little rain or snow falls.

There are many factors that affect the climate of an area. Two of these factors are **latitude** and nearness to ocean currents.

Latitude is the distance north or south of the **equator**. The equator is an imaginary line that divides Earth into the Northern Hemisphere and the Southern Hemisphere. The nearer a place is to the equator, the lower its latitude. Places near the equator have tropical climates. The places farthest from the equator have polar climates.

A current is a moving stream of water in an ocean. The Gulf Stream is a current of warm water. It moves north along the east coast of the United States. This current warms the nearby land areas. Cold ocean currents make land areas cooler.

Comprehension and Vocabulary Review

➤ **Darken the circle by the best answer.**

1. _____ is the distance north or south of the equator.
   - Ⓐ Weather
   - Ⓑ Climate
   - Ⓒ Latitude
   - Ⓓ Current

2. _____ is the average weather of a region over a long period of time.
   - Ⓐ Climate
   - Ⓑ Latitude
   - Ⓒ Current
   - Ⓓ Equator

3. This article is mainly about _____.
   - Ⓐ rain and snow
   - Ⓑ the Gulf Stream
   - Ⓒ weather in the United States
   - Ⓓ the different climate zones in the world

4. Warm ocean currents make the nearby land areas _____.
   - Ⓐ colder
   - Ⓑ warmer
   - Ⓒ rainy
   - Ⓓ windy

5. You can conclude that the places farthest from the equator have _____ climates.
   - Ⓐ hot
   - Ⓑ warm
   - Ⓒ cold
   - Ⓓ wet

6. The _____ is an imaginary line around the center of Earth.
   - Ⓐ climate
   - Ⓑ equator
   - Ⓒ current
   - Ⓓ factor

➤ **Write complete sentences to answer the question.**

7. What are two of the factors that affect the climate of an area?

   _____

   _____

Nonfiction Comprehension: Grades 3–4, SV 8947-8

Classification Organizer

A tree diagram helps you to classify information, or put it in groups. The diagram starts with a general group. As you move down the tree diagram, the groups become more specific. The last part of the tree should be details about each group.

 Complete the tree diagram about climate zones. Name the three main climate zones. Then give details about the kind of climate found in each zone.

```
                    ┌─────────────────────┐
                    │    Climate Zones     │
                    └─────────────────────┘
```

Zone:	Zone:	Zone:
Details:	Details:	Details:

 Write a complete sentence to answer the question.

In which climate zone do you live?

_____

_____

Nonfiction Comprehension: Grades 3–4, SV 8947-8

Types of Sharks

There are many types of sharks. Many sharks are fairly large, such as the great hammerhead and great white, which are 15 to 20 feet long. The largest shark is the whale shark, which averages 40 feet long. The smallest shark is the pygmy dogfish, which is only 5 or 6 inches long.

Some sharks are very dangerous. The great white shark is probably the best-known and most dangerous shark. It lives in cool temperate and tropical waters. Great white sharks are feared because they have attacked people many times.

Great White Shark

The whale shark and the basking shark are not dangerous to people. These large sharks do not even eat other fish. They eat tiny ocean plants and animals called **plankton**. The basking shark floats on the surface as if it is basking in the sun.

The hammerhead shark is an **unusual** shark. Its head is T-shaped, like the head of a hammer. Its eyes are on each end of the crossbar of the *T*. Hammerheads are found in tropical oceans. They sometimes travel in **schools**.

Dogfish are small sharks that live in temperate or tropical seas. Unlike the great white shark, which gives birth to live young, the dogfish lays eggs. The eggs are in cases that cling to seaweed until they hatch. Like most other fish, young sharks can take care of themselves from birth.

Hammerhead Shark

Name _____ Date_____

Comprehension Review

➡ **Darken the circle by the best answer.**

1. The whale shark and the _____ eat plankton.
   Ⓐ great white shark
   Ⓑ dogfish
   Ⓒ basking shark
   Ⓓ hammerhead shark

5. The smallest shark is the pygmy _____, which is 5 or 6 inches long.
   Ⓐ dogfish
   Ⓑ whale shark
   Ⓒ basking shark
   Ⓓ hammerhead shark

2. The dogfish lays eggs in cases that cling to _____ until they hatch.
   Ⓐ their mother
   Ⓑ seaweed
   Ⓒ other fish
   Ⓓ whales

6. The largest shark is the _____, which averages 40 feet long.
   Ⓐ great white shark
   Ⓑ whale shark
   Ⓒ basking shark
   Ⓓ hammerhead shark

3. The main purpose of this article is to tell _____.
   Ⓐ how mean sharks are
   Ⓑ how long sharks grow
   Ⓒ what sharks eat
   Ⓓ about the different kinds of sharks

7. Hammerhead sharks are unusual because _____.
   Ⓐ they like to build wooden things
   Ⓑ they have long fingernails
   Ⓒ they have T-shaped heads
   Ⓓ they never eat

4. Plankton are _____.
   Ⓐ small boards
   Ⓑ tiny ocean plants and animals
   Ⓒ seashells
   Ⓓ a kind of shark

8. The great white shark's young are _____.
   Ⓐ born live
   Ⓑ hatched from eggs
   Ⓒ dogfish
   Ⓓ friendly to humans

Lesson 13: Classification
Nonfiction Comprehension: Grades 3–4, SV 8947-8

Comparison-Contrast

BEFORE READING

Tap Prior Knowledge

"Probability": Ask the students if they have ever flipped a coin to see if it would come up heads or tails. The likelihood that it will come up one or the other is called probability.

"Eagles and Hawks": Ask the students if they know what the national bird of the United States is (eagle). Have they ever seen an eagle? Have they ever seen a hawk?

"Weird and Wonderful Lizards": Ask the students if they have ever seen a lizard. Likely they will have seen some of the more common kinds of lizards, such as a gecko. Ask the students about the characteristics of lizards.

Skill to Emphasize

Review the section about comparison-contrast on page 82. Tell the students that *compare* means to show how things are alike, and *contrast* means to show how things are different.

DURING READING

Preview Text Features

Point out the sidebar in "Probability." It gives information that will help the students to understand probability. The illustrations in the "Weird and Wonderful Lizards" article help the students to envision the two kinds of lizards being discussed. Boldfaced words indicate vocabulary words.

Comprehending the Selection

Model a better understanding of comparison-contrast by asking: *In what ways are the two things alike and different?*

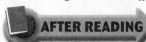
AFTER READING

Reinforce the Comprehension Skill

Tell the students that comparison-contrast helps them to understand how two things are alike and different. The two things are of the same general group, so they have basic common features. The differences are what allow the students to tell one thing from the other. Distribute copies of the Venn Diagram on page 123 to help the students organize the information.

Assess

Have the students complete the activities for the selections.

WRITE ABOUT IT

Distribute copies of the Venn Diagram on page 123. Have the students choose two simple items to compare and contrast, such as dogs and cats or pies and cakes. Have them include at least three points on which they will compare and contrast the two items. Then have them write a short comparison-contrast essay using the information they have compiled in their Venn Diagram.

AT HOME

Search through the newspaper or news magazines for articles about eagles and hawks. Bring these articles to school to share with the class.

SELECTION DETAILS

Summary

"Probability" (page 90) compares and contrasts dependent and independent probability.

"Eagles and Hawks" (page 91) compares and contrasts the two kinds of birds.

"Weird and Wonderful Lizards" (page 93) compares and contrasts the ways that two amazing lizards stay safe and hunt for food.

Selection Type

Mathematics Article
Science Articles

Comprehension Skill

Identify Comparison-Contrast in a Nonfiction Article

Standards

Reading
• Understand the use of comparison and contrast in a nonfiction selection.
• Identify details in a reading selection.

Mathematics
• Understand the difference between dependent and independent probability.

Science
• Know adaptations that allow animals to survive.

VOCABULARY

Introduce the vocabulary words and write them on the board. Help students find a definition for each word. Have students use each word in a sentence.

"Probability"
probability   independent
dependent

"Eagles and Hawks"
carnivorous   talons
soaring   damage

"Weird and Wonderful Lizards"
scales   shed
predator   camouflage
sway   crest
prey   grasp

Probability

Probability is the chance that an event will happen. Suppose you flip a penny. You have one chance of flipping heads and one chance of flipping tails. You can write the probability of flipping heads or tails like this: $\frac{1}{2}$, or 1 in 2. No matter how many times you flip the penny, the probability of flipping heads or tails is always $\frac{1}{2}$. This type of probability is called **independent**.

$\dfrac{1}{2}$ $\dfrac{\text{heads side}}{\text{sides of a penny}}$

$\dfrac{1}{2}$ $\dfrac{\text{tails side}}{\text{sides of a penny}}$

$\dfrac{1}{3}$ $\dfrac{\text{pink marble}}{\text{marbles in bag}}$

$\dfrac{1}{2}$ $\dfrac{\text{pink marble}}{\text{marbles in bag}}$

Suppose you have 2 blue marbles and one pink marble in a bag. The chance of picking a pink marble is 1 in 3, or $\frac{1}{3}$. If you pick a blue marble, only a blue marble and pink marble will be left. The probability of picking a pink marble is now $\frac{1}{2}$. The probability has changed. It depends on how many marbles are left in the bag. This type of probability is called **dependent**.

 Write a complete sentence to answer each question.

1. What is probability?

_____

2. Are independent and dependent probability alike or different?

_____

3. How are they alike or different?

_____

_____

_____

_____

_____

Nonfiction Comprehension: Grades 3–4, SV 8947-8

Eagles and Hawks

Eagles and hawks are **carnivorous** birds. They eat other animals. They both have long, sharp claws called **talons** to grab and hold their food. Eagles and hawks also have sharp, curved beaks for cutting and tearing meat.

Eagles and hawks are very good fliers. They spend much of their time **soaring** in the air. Soaring is flying without flapping the wings. Eagles and hawks can soar for hours.

Eagles and hawks have good eyesight. They can spot a mouse while they are flying hundreds of feet above the ground.

Red-tailed Hawk

Hawks are smaller than eagles, and they eat smaller animals. Some small hawks eat insects, snakes, or frogs. The red-tailed hawk can find food while soaring in the air. Then it dives toward the ground at about 120 miles an hour. The red-tailed hawk eats mice, snakes, birds, and other small animals.

Some eagles catch and eat fish. A few eagles are so big that they can catch monkeys and small deer. Many eagles and hawks eat mice and rabbits. Mice and rabbits can **damage** farm crops. Although eagles and hawks help farmers by eating mice and rabbits, some people shoot these birds. There are now laws against shooting eagles and hawks.

Eagles and hawks build very big nests. Some can be 6 feet wide and 3 feet deep. Some eagles and hawks build their nests in trees. Others nest on cliffs or on the ground.

Golden Eagle

Nonfiction Comprehension: Grades 3–4, SV 8947-8

Name _____ Date_____

Comprehension and Vocabulary Review

➡ **Darken the circle by the best answer.**

1. Hawks and eagles help farmers by eating _____.
   Ⓐ corn
   Ⓑ cows
   Ⓒ worms
   Ⓓ mice

2. After a hawk finds food while soaring, it _____.
   Ⓐ dives toward the ground
   Ⓑ crashes into a tree
   Ⓒ looks for other food
   Ⓓ builds a nest

3. This article is mostly about _____.
   Ⓐ how eagles build nests
   Ⓑ how eagles and hawks have good eyesight
   Ⓒ how eagles and hawks are alike and different
   Ⓓ what eagles and hawks eat

4. A carnivorous animal eats _____.
   Ⓐ only plants
   Ⓑ corn
   Ⓒ meat
   Ⓓ claws

5. Eagles and hawks use their _____ to grab and hold their food.
   Ⓐ forks
   Ⓑ hands
   Ⓒ wings
   Ⓓ talons

6. Eagles and hawks use their _____ to cut and tear meat.
   Ⓐ talons
   Ⓑ bears
   Ⓒ beads
   Ⓓ beaks

7. Eagles and hawks spend much of their time _____ in the air.
   Ⓐ sleeping
   Ⓑ soaring
   Ⓒ dancing
   Ⓓ building nests

8. Some eagles are so big they can catch and eat _____.
   Ⓐ crops
   Ⓑ deer
   Ⓒ horses
   Ⓓ people

www.harcourtschoolsupply.com
© Harcourt Achieve Inc. All rights reserved.

92

Lesson 14: Comparison-Contrast
Nonfiction Comprehension: Grades 3–4, SV 8947-8

Weird and Wonderful Lizards

There are many different kinds of lizards. But they are the same in some ways. All lizards are reptiles. Reptiles cannot keep themselves warm. Lizards often lie in the sunlight to warm their bodies. Also, all lizards have dry skin covered with **scales**. They **shed** this skin as they grow. Two weird and wonderful lizards are the frilled lizard and the veiled chameleon (kuh MEEL yuhn). Like all lizards, they both have scales and shed skin. They are also alike because they both live in trees.

Staying Alive

There are some big, hungry animals that like to eat lizards. A lizard is always watching for a **predator** that is looking for food. The frilled lizard and the veiled chameleon have different body parts and different ways to keep themselves safe.

The frilled lizard gets its name from the flap of skin around its neck. The color of its skin looks like the tree trunks on which it lives. This special ability to blend in with the surroundings is called **camouflage**. Camouflage helps the frilled lizard hide from hungry predators.

If camouflage doesn't work, the frilled lizard has another way to protect itself. The frilled lizard opens its mouth very wide. Then the flap of skin opens like an umbrella around its head. This frilled flap makes the lizard look bigger than it really is.

Frilled Lizard

If the predator still does not go away, the frilled lizard will stand on its two back legs and **sway** from side to side. It beats its long tail on the ground and jumps toward the predator. When all else fails, the frilled lizard turns and runs away on its back legs!

Nonfiction Comprehension: Grades 3–4, SV 8947-8

Unlike the frilled lizard, the veiled chameleon moves very slowly. It does not have any body parts that can scare away a predator. The veiled chameleon does use camouflage to stay safe but in a different way from the frilled lizard. Its body is green with yellow, orange, and blue stripes. It also has a **crest** on its head. When the veiled chameleon sits in a tree, its body will shake like a leaf blowing in the wind. It can hide from a predator by blending in with the other leaves.

Chameleon

On the Hunt

The frilled lizard and the veiled chameleon both eat insects. But they have different ways to hunt for food. The frilled lizard is a fast runner. It sees a tasty treat and runs to catch it with its mouth. However, the veiled chameleon sits very still and watches. It is too slow to run. The chameleon's eyes can move in two different directions. One eye will look for its **prey**, while the other eye looks for danger.

When the veiled chameleon sees an insect, it slowly moves toward it. Its long toes help it **grasp** tree branches. It also has a long tail. When it walks or hunts for food, the veiled chameleon uses its tail to hold onto the tree branch. When the veiled chameleon is near its prey, its sticky tongue darts out to catch the insect! There are many other weird and wonderful lizards. Each lizard has its own amazing ways to stay safe and hunt for food.

Comprehension Review

Name _____ Date _____

 Darken the circle by the best answer.

1. All lizards are alike because they
   _____.
   Ⓐ have fur
   Ⓑ are reptiles
   Ⓒ fly
   Ⓓ live underwater

2. Lizards _____ as they grow.
   Ⓐ get smaller
   Ⓑ grow more legs
   Ⓒ shed their skin
   Ⓓ learn to sing

3. The author wrote this article
   mainly to _____.
   Ⓐ entertain readers with a funny
      story about lizards
   Ⓑ ask readers to buy pet lizards
   Ⓒ tell about how chameleons
      change colors
   Ⓓ tell readers about two kinds of
      lizards

4. When the frilled lizard sways, its
   body _____.
   Ⓐ falls apart
   Ⓑ moves back and forth
   Ⓒ rises into the air
   Ⓓ explodes

5. Lizards lie in the sunlight because
   _____.
   Ⓐ they have scales
   Ⓑ they need a way to warm their
      bodies
   Ⓒ the sunlight makes them shed
      their skin
   Ⓓ they are waiting for food to
      walk by

6. What would be another good title
   for this article?
   Ⓐ The Veiled Chameleon
   Ⓑ Two Amazing Lizards
   Ⓒ The Life of the Frilled Lizard
   Ⓓ All About Reptiles

Write a complete sentence to answer the question.

7. Why would the open flap of skin on the frilled lizard scare away a
   predator?

   _____

   _____

   _____

Nonfiction Comprehension: Grades 3–4, SV 8947-8

Vocabulary Review

➤ Write a vocabulary word from the box to complete each sentence.

> camouflage   crest   grasp   predator   prey   sway

A veiled chameleon was warming itself in the sun. Suddenly, it spotted a

scary _____ looking for food. The lizard did not want to be the
        1

bird's _____. The chameleon slowly wrapped its tail around a
        2

tree branch. Then it used its long claws to _____ the branch.
                                               3

The chameleon began to _____ slowly. With its bright colors
                          4

and the _____ on its head, the chameleon looked just like a
        5

leaf. The chameleon had used _____ to save its life.
                               6

Build Your Vocabulary

Some words can have more than one meaning.

➤ Read each word and its meanings. Write the letter of the meaning for each underlined word.

> **scales a.** Thin, flat plates that cover the body of some animals. **b.** Tools used to find out how much things weigh.
> **shed c.** To lose or fall off naturally. **d.** A small building that is used to store things.

____ **7.** We looked for a hammer inside the tool <u>shed</u>.

____ **8.** The farmer used <u>scales</u> to weigh the fruit.

____ **9.** The young lizard was about to <u>shed</u> its skin.

____ **10.** The garden snake had smooth, dry <u>scales</u>.

Nonfiction Comprehension: Grades 3–4, SV 8947-8

Name _____ Date_____

Comparing and Contrasting Lizards

Writers compare to show how two things are alike. They contrast to show how those things are different. A tool for comparing and contrasting is a Venn diagram. A Venn diagram is shown below.

▬▶ **Use the article about lizards to complete the diagram. Under each lizard's name, write details that tell about that lizard. Under "Both," write details that tell about both lizards.**

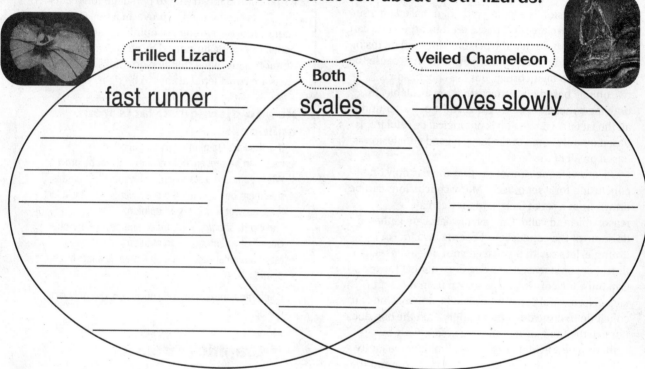

Frilled Lizard

Both

Veiled Chameleon

fast runner

scales

moves slowly

▬▶ **Use the article and your diagram to write the answers. Write complete sentences.**

1. Write two details that tell how the two lizards are alike.

_____

_____

2. Write two details that tell how the two lizards are different.

_____

_____

Lesson 14: Comparison-Contrast
Nonfiction Comprehension: Grades 3–4, SV 8947-8

UNIT 6 Conclusion

Sometimes an author may not tell the reader directly what is happening in an article. Sometimes the reader must make a conclusion based on the facts of the article or the reader's own experiences or observations. After making a conclusion, the reader may need to change it if additional facts and details are gathered. Sometimes the reader must also conclude if a writer's statement is a fact or an opinion.

• Drawing Conclusions (Lesson 15)

A conclusion is a logical judgment based on a set of facts. If there are mud tracks on the carpet, one can logically conclude that the person with mud on his or her shoes made those tracks. New facts may cause the conclusion to be incorrect, but the conclusion is reasonable based on the facts that are available. In drawing conclusions, the reader must pay attention to all the facts. A conclusion is not logical or valid if it is based on only some of the facts; a good conclusion is based on all of the facts.

However, one cannot say that there is only one conclusion for a set of facts. Many conclusions can be drawn from a set of facts, and they can all be reasonable and valid. Only as new facts are gathered do some of the conclusions become invalid. For example, let's say that you feed your dog at its regular time. For some reason, the dog does not eat the food. Can only one conclusion be drawn from this set of facts? No, several conclusions can be drawn. One can conclude that the dog is not hungry, that the dog does not like the food, or that the dog is sick. Only by gathering new evidence can one eliminate the faulty conclusions. If you take the dog to the doctor and the doctor says the dog is not sick, you have eliminated one conclusion based on new evidence. If you feed the dog the same food at another time and it eats the food then, you can conclude that the dog was not hungry the first time. Based on the new set of facts, this conclusion is logical and valid.

To draw logical conclusions:
- Read the information carefully.
- Think about the facts and your own experiences and observations.
- Decide what all the facts tell you.
- Write a conclusion based on the facts you have available.
- Be sure your conclusion uses all the facts, not just some.
- Change your conclusion if new facts show something different.

• Fact or Opinion? (Lesson 16)

Nonfiction articles contain facts. Nonfiction articles sometimes also give opinions, or a person's beliefs. Facts are used to inform, and opinions are used to persuade. Sometimes a reader must decide, or conclude, if a statement is a fact or an opinion. Writers often use facts to support their opinions. They want to convince the reader that what they are claiming is true. If an article contains opinions, the writer is probably trying to persuade the reader.

Facts can be used to prove an issue. Opinions cannot prove anything. An opinion is simply a person's belief, often not supported by facts of any kind. The opinion is just what that person thinks, right or wrong. Facts are considered always to be right.

How to distinguish facts from opinions:
- Use the Fact-Opinion Chart on page 124.
- Facts can be proven, but opinions cannot be proven.
- When you read a statement, ask yourself, "Can this statement be proven?" If the answer is *yes*, it is a fact. If the answer is *no*, it is an opinion.
- The words *should*, *must*, *think*, and *believe* are often clues that a sentence is an opinion.
- Make a mental note that a statement is a fact or an opinion.
- If you must make a logical conclusion, use only facts, not opinions.

• Graphic Organizer

Fact-Opinion Chart   page 124

Research Base

"Content literacy involves knowing what to expect—anticipating the kinds of organizational structures the reader might encounter. Content literacy also involves understanding the kinds of graphic features the reader needs to interpret, as well as vocabulary specific to the topic. The reader uses the text's organization, language, and visual features in a unified way to derive meaning. In other words students must learn how to read history, biology, environmental science, geographical descriptions, and other kinds of texts." (*Guiding Readers and Writers: Grades 3–6*, p. 400)

Drawing Conclusions

Summary
"Clouds" (page 100) discusses the three main cloud types.

"Florence Kelley: A Voice for the Children" (page 102) discusses the efforts of Florence Kelley to regulate child labor in the late 1800s.

"Land and People of Latin America" (page 106) provides information on the landforms, climate, people, history, and culture of the region known as Latin America.

Selection Type
Science Article
Social Studies Articles

Comprehension Skill
Draw Conclusions from Facts in a Nonfiction Article

Standards
Reading
• Draw conclusions from texts.
Science
• Explore the three basic cloud types.
Social Studies
• Learn about an important reformer working to pass child-labor laws.
• Study the region of Latin America.

VOCABULARY

Introduce the vocabulary words and write them on the board. Help students find a definition for each word. Have students use each word in a sentence.
"Clouds"
condenses   cirrus
cumulus   stratus
"Florence Kelley: A Voice for the Children"
horror   acid
labor   inspector
smallpox
"Land and People of Latin America"
elevation   developing nations
sea level   subsistence farmers
mestizos   natural resources
plantations

Tap Prior Knowledge
"Clouds": The students will know about clouds, but ask them if they know what kind of weather each cloud type foretells.

"Florence Kelley: A Voice for the Children": Ask the students if they would rather go to school or work all day. A hundred years ago, children often did not have a choice. They had to work, often in places that were unsafe.

"Land and People of Latin America": Ask the students if any have been to Mexico or the countries south of Mexico. Ask the students if they know the similarities and differences between Latin America and their country. Where would they rather live?

Skill to Emphasize
Review the section about drawing conclusions on page 98. Tell the students that writers sometimes do not tell the reader everything that is happening in an article. The reader must sometimes draw conclusions, or make judgments, about the facts given.

Preview Text Features
Have the students look at the cloud illustrations in the "Clouds" article. Have the students look at the map in the "Land and People of Latin America" article. It gives the location of the region of Latin America. Boldfaced words indicate vocabulary words.

Comprehending the Selection
Model a better understanding of conclusion by asking: *Using the facts given, what conclusions can you make about the topic?*

Reinforce the Comprehension Skill
Tell the students that a good conclusion is based on all the facts of the article. They should be sure their conclusions make sense and include all the facts.

Assess
Have the students complete the activities for the selections.

WRITE ABOUT IT

Have the students write a paragraph telling why they think history is or is not an important thing to know about.

Clouds

A cloud is a mass of water droplets or ice crystals that floats in the air. When warm air rises and cools, the water vapor in air **condenses** and forms water droplets. These droplets form clouds.

There are three main types of clouds. They are cirrus, cumulus, and stratus. These types of clouds may combine to form many other kinds of clouds. You can study clouds to find out how the weather will change.

Cirrus clouds are white and feathery. They form high in the sky. It is so cold in this part of the atmosphere that cirrus clouds are made entirely of ice crystals. Cirrus clouds usually mean that rain or snow is coming within a day.

Cumulus clouds are thick, white, and fluffy. They look like piles of cotton. You can often see cumulus clouds on a sunny summer day. They mean fair weather. Cumulus clouds form much lower in the atmosphere than cirrus clouds and are made only of water droplets.

Stratus clouds are layers of gray clouds that cover most of the sky. They often mean that rain or snow is coming. Stratus clouds form low in the atmosphere. A stratus cloud that forms on the ground is called fog. Fog forms when air that is holding a lot of water cools off quickly at night.

Sometimes the term *nimbus* is added to the name of a cloud. *Nimbus* means that a cloud is heavy and dark and will bring rain. Cumulonimbus clouds, for example, produce summer thunderstorms.

100

Comprehension and Vocabulary Review

→ **Darken the circle by the best answer.**

1. Cumulus clouds look like _____.
   Ⓐ piles of black coal
   Ⓑ piles of white cotton
   Ⓒ piles of green plants
   Ⓓ piles of red roses

2. You can study clouds to find out how the _____ will change.
   Ⓐ weather
   Ⓑ Moon
   Ⓒ stars
   Ⓓ fog

3. A _____ cloud that forms on the ground is called fog.
   Ⓐ cumulus
   Ⓑ cirrus
   Ⓒ stratus
   Ⓓ cotton

4. _____ means that a cloud is heavy and dark and will bring rain.
   Ⓐ *Nimbus*
   Ⓑ *Cumulus*
   Ⓒ *Cirrus*
   Ⓓ *Stratus*

5. Cirrus clouds are made entirely of _____.
   Ⓐ cotton
   Ⓑ ice crystals
   Ⓒ fog
   Ⓓ feathers

6. If you see cirrus clouds, you can conclude that _____.
   Ⓐ fair weather is coming
   Ⓑ there was fog yesterday
   Ⓒ a heat wave is coming
   Ⓓ rain or snow is coming within a day

7. If you see cumulus clouds, you can conclude that _____.
   Ⓐ fair weather is coming
   Ⓑ there was snow yesterday
   Ⓒ a tornado is on the way
   Ⓓ rain or snow is coming soon

8. If you see very low stratus clouds, you can conclude that _____.
   Ⓐ fair weather is on the way
   Ⓑ there will be fog
   Ⓒ the weather will be hot and dry
   Ⓓ it will soon be night

Florence Kelley: A Voice for the Children

Florence Kelley stared in **horror** at the giant room full of furnaces. "So this is what a glass factory is like," she thought. The only light came from the flaming furnaces. In front of these furnaces, glass blowers sat working. Dozens of young boys hurried around. They carried heavy buckets of water or sat next to the furnaces, cleaning tools. The boys looked tired and dirty. They had cuts and burns from the hot glass.

Florence Kelley was only 12 years old when she visited this glass factory. Her father took her there. He wanted to show her the wonders of new factories. He wanted her to see how quickly things were made. But Kelley also saw how awful the factory was for child workers. She could not forget the small boys crouching by the hot furnaces. "It was a picture I carried with me all my days," she later wrote.

Later, Kelley learned that over one million children worked in factories. The factories were hot, crowded, and unsafe. Many children worked 12 hours a day, six or seven days a week. Factory owners didn't have to pay children as much as older workers. Every year tens of thousands of child workers were hurt or killed. In some factories, children handled pots of **acid** or boiling water. Often they were badly burned. Some children ran large machines. Some of these children lost fingers, arms, or legs. Most factories had no fresh air. There was no protection from dirt and disease. Many factory owners locked their doors. If a fire broke out, the workers inside could not escape. Many child workers died.

"Something must be done!" said Kelley. In 1889, she wrote a paper. She told of the horrors children faced in factories. She asked all Americans to help change things. "Do not buy goods made by child workers!" she cried. "Buy from companies that don't hire children!"

Kelley also asked the government to help. She wanted new laws. She wanted a law keeping all children under 16 years old in school. Kelley spoke to anyone who would listen. In a few years, she was famous. Everyone knew her as a leader in the fight against child **labor**.

In 1893, Florence Kelley fought for a new law. The law said factory owners could not hire young children. The law also created a Chief Factory **Inspector** to make sure factories were following the new law.

The governor of Illinois asked her to be the Chief Factory Inspector. Kelley's first months as Inspector were not easy. Day after day she traveled to dark, dirty factories. She ordered the factory owners to stop using young workers. Owners hated to see Kelley coming. Many were rude to her. One took out his gun. He fired a couple of warning shots. He thought it would scare her off. But he was wrong. Kelley's life was in danger, but she would not stop her work. She cared more about the safety of children than she did about her own safety.

Then **smallpox** broke out. Many people died. It was easily passed from one person to another. It could be passed on in clothing. The way to stop smallpox was to keep sick people away from everyone else. Clothing made by sick people should also be kept away.

"Sick people are sewing clothes," Kelley thought. "They are passing the disease on to child workers. The clothes they make are sold in stores. People buy the clothes and carry smallpox home."

Kelley knew she had to act. She made sick workers stop working. She also got rid of the clothes they had made. "Burn them!" she ordered owners. Thousands of dollars worth of clothing were burned. Factory owners were very angry. Still, Kelley did not back down.

When Florence Kelley's time as Inspector was over, there was still much to be done. Yet Kelley had started to change the way people think. People began to see that it was wrong to use child workers. Florence Kelley never gave up the fight to protect America's children.

Comprehension Review

➡️ **Darken the circle by the best answer.**

1. When Florence Kelley was 12 years old, she saw boys working in a _____.
   - Ⓐ circus
   - Ⓑ school
   - Ⓒ factory
   - Ⓓ store

2. After Florence Kelley got a law passed in 1893, she _____.
   - Ⓐ became President of the United States
   - Ⓑ became the Chief Factory Inspector
   - Ⓒ got a job in a factory
   - Ⓓ wrote a book

3. This article is mainly about _____.
   - Ⓐ how children can earn money
   - Ⓑ how mean factory owners are
   - Ⓒ a woman who helped children
   - Ⓓ an outbreak of smallpox

4. You can conclude from the article that Kelley thought children should _____.
   - Ⓐ stay at home
   - Ⓑ work in factories all the time
   - Ⓒ be in school
   - Ⓓ work part-time

➡️ **Write a conclusion to finish each sentence.**

5. Many child workers lost their lives in factory fires because _____
   _____.

6. Factory owners hated to see Kelley coming because _____
   _____.

7. Kelley made factory owners burn thousands of dollars worth of clothes because _____
   _____.

Name _____ Date_____

Vocabulary Review

 Darken the circle by the best meaning for the word in dark print.

1. Florence Kelley felt **horror** when she saw the glass factory.
   - Ⓐ fear and dislike
   - Ⓑ joy
   - Ⓒ cold
   - Ⓓ tired and dirty

2. The factory room was full of **furnaces**.
   - Ⓐ clothes
   - Ⓑ workers
   - Ⓒ children
   - Ⓓ fireplaces

3. Kelley saw small boys **crouching** by the hot furnaces.
   - Ⓐ sleeping
   - Ⓑ bending down
   - Ⓒ eating
   - Ⓓ standing up

4. Some children handled pots of **acid**.
   - Ⓐ a chemical that can burn you
   - Ⓑ soup
   - Ⓒ glass blowers
   - Ⓓ paint

5. Kelley worked against child **labor**.
   - Ⓐ schooling
   - Ⓑ rights
   - Ⓒ work
   - Ⓓ clothes

6. Kelley served as the Chief Factory **Inspector**.
   - Ⓐ one who checks that things are done correctly
   - Ⓑ one who cooks food in a cafeteria
   - Ⓒ one who works in a cave
   - Ⓓ one who makes glasses

7. Some factory workers were **rude** to Kelley.
   - Ⓐ ready to help
   - Ⓑ kind
   - Ⓒ friendly
   - Ⓓ not polite

8. Many people were dying of **smallpox**.
   - Ⓐ a kind of snack
   - Ⓑ a disease
   - Ⓒ a factory tool
   - Ⓓ a kind of job

Land and People of Latin America

Which part of the world has the longest mountain chain? Which region has the most Spanish-speaking people? From where in the world do we get most of our coffee and bananas? The answer to all of these questions is Latin America.

Landforms of Latin America

Latin America includes all of the nations south of the United States. This region is called Latin America because most people speak Spanish or Portuguese. Both of these languages developed from Latin. Latin is a very old language that few people speak today.

Find Latin America on the map. Latin America has three parts. The islands in the Caribbean Sea form one part. Middle America is another part. This part includes Mexico and the countries of Central America. The third and largest part is the continent of South America.

Mountains cover large areas of Latin America. Some of these mountains are volcanoes. The tall Andes Mountains are in the west of South America. The Andes mountain chain is the longest one in the world. Plains and plateaus cover other parts of Latin America. There are important rivers in South America. The longest river in

South America is the Amazon River. Other large rivers join the Amazon. Many people use these rivers for transportation.

The Tropics

Most of Latin America is in a region called the tropics. This is a hot region near the equator. The equator is an imaginary line that divides the globe in half. The halves are called the Northern Hemisphere and the Southern Hemisphere. The equator is the line of latitude that is 0°. The plains near the equator have a tropical climate. A tropical climate is hot all the time. It is hot because this region receives more direct sunlight for a longer period of time than other parts of the world. It is also very rainy in the tropics.

Latin America has the world's largest tropical rain forest. These thick forests are found near the equator. They grow where the climate is very hot and very wet. The largest tropical rain forest is in South America. Smaller tropical rain forests can be found in Middle America and on islands in the Caribbean Sea.

Many parts of Latin America have cooler climates even though they are in the tropics. This is because of their **elevation**. Elevation tells you how high the land is above **sea level**. The climate becomes colder as the land's elevation gets higher. Some very tall mountains in the tropics are always covered with snow.

There are two other reasons why some parts of Latin America have cooler climates. First, the southern part of South America is very far from the equator. As you move away from the equator, the climate becomes colder. The second reason is that ocean winds give the coastal plains and the islands in the Caribbean Sea milder climates.

History, People, and Culture

Indians were the first people to live in Latin America. Five groups of Indians built great nations in Latin America. They built good roads and large cities.

Five hundred years ago people from Spain conquered most of Latin America. They forced Indians to be their slaves. Millions of Indians died while working for the Spanish. Then the Spanish brought slaves from Africa to work in Latin America.

Name _____ Date_____

Spain ruled most of Latin America. But Portugal ruled the huge nation of Brazil. Other countries in Europe also ruled smaller colonies. In the early 1800s, Latin Americans fought to rule themselves. By 1826, most countries were free.

Who are the people of Latin America today? Some are white people whose families came from Europe. Some people are Indians. Most people are **mestizos**. A mestizo is a person who has European and Indian ancestors. There are also many black people in the Caribbean countries and in Brazil.

The Spanish culture is important in most of Latin America. People in most countries speak Spanish. The Spanish brought the Catholic religion to the region. Today most Latin Americans are Catholics.

Almost three fourths of the people in Latin America live in cities. Some of the world's largest cities are in Latin America. Most of the cities are found on the plateaus and the coastal plains of Latin America. It is hard to live in tall mountains or in tropical rain forests. So these areas of Latin America have small populations.

Earning a Living

Most countries in Latin America are **developing nations**. A developing nation is a nation with a low standard of living and not much industry. In the cities most people work at service jobs. Some people work in factories. Many people in Latin America are farmers.

There are two kinds of farmers in Latin America. There are poor **subsistence farmers** who work on small farms. They try to grow enough food for their families. The second kind of farmer grows cash crops. Coffee, bananas, and sugar cane are important cash crops in Latin America. Cash crops are grown on huge farms called **plantations**. A very small part of the population owns most of the plantations. Millions of poor farmers work on the plantations.

Latin America has many **natural resources**. Some countries have metals such as silver and copper. In these countries many people work in mines. A few countries like Mexico and Venezuela have oil. But there is little iron and coal in Latin America. These two resources are needed to make cars, trucks, and other machines. This is one reason why there is not much industry in Latin America.

Nonfiction Comprehension: Grades 3–4, SV 8947-8

Comprehension and Vocabulary Review

➡ **Darken the circle by the best answer.**

1. In most Latin American countries, people speak _____.
   - Ⓐ French
   - Ⓑ English
   - Ⓒ Latin
   - Ⓓ Spanish

2. After Spain conquered most of Latin America, _____.
   - Ⓐ the Spanish forced the Indians to be their slaves
   - Ⓑ the Spanish left
   - Ⓒ the Spanish built a factory for blowing glass
   - Ⓓ mountains formed

3. This article is mostly about _____.
   - Ⓐ Spanish explorers
   - Ⓑ the Amazon River
   - Ⓒ the landforms and people of Latin America
   - Ⓓ good jobs in Latin America

4. _____ have European and Indian ancestors.
   - Ⓐ Andes
   - Ⓑ Mestizos
   - Ⓒ Subsistence
   - Ⓓ Plantations

5. You can conclude that subsistence farmers _____.
   - Ⓐ have too many tractors
   - Ⓑ do not work at sea level
   - Ⓒ do not grow food to sell
   - Ⓓ own large plantations

6. A hemisphere is _____.
   - Ⓐ a small balloon
   - Ⓑ half of a globe
   - Ⓒ a kind of egg
   - Ⓓ a spear that belongs to him

7. The world's longest mountain chain is the _____.
   - Ⓐ Amazon
   - Ⓑ Equator
   - Ⓒ Andes
   - Ⓓ Elevation

8. _____ means how high the land is above sea level.
   - Ⓐ Equator
   - Ⓑ Elevation
   - Ⓒ Subsistence
   - Ⓓ Latin

Nonfiction Comprehension: Grades 3–4, SV 8947-8

Drawing Conclusions

Read the first two sentences below. Then read the third sentence. Notice how it follows from the first two sentences. The third sentence is called a conclusion.

There are mountains in Middle America.
There are mountains in South America.
Conclusion: Many parts of Latin America have mountains.

➤ **Read each pair of sentences. Then look in the box for the conclusion you might make. Write the letter of the conclusion on the line.**

Conclusions
A. There are many kinds of people in Latin America.
B. The Spanish brought their language and religion to Latin America.
C. Some parts of the tropics have cooler climates.
D. Many nations in Latin America are developing nations.

1. Tall mountains near the equator are covered with snow.
   Ocean winds cool the islands in the Caribbean Sea.

   Conclusion: ____

2. The first people in Latin America were Indians. Later, people from Europe and Africa came to Latin America.

   Conclusion: ____

3. Many people in Latin America have a low standard of living. Most countries in Latin America do not have much industry.

   Conclusion: ____

4. Most people in Latin America speak Spanish. Most people in Latin America are Catholics.

   Conclusion: ____

Writing About It

➤ Write a paragraph that tells about landforms, rivers, and tropical rain forests of Latin America. Use another piece of paper.

Fact or Opinion?

BEFORE READING

SELECTION DETAILS

Summary

"Chief Tecumseh" (page 112) tells about this chief who fought treaties that took lands from the American Indians.

"Save the Rain Forests!" (page 114) discusses how rain forests are rich sources of plant and animal life. This article tells how scientists study the rain forests and why it is important to protect them.

Selection Type
Social Studies Articles

Comprehension Skill
Distinguish Fact from Opinion

Standards

Reading
- Distinguish fact from opinion in various texts.
- Use the organizational features of texts to locate information.

Social Studies
- Explore cultural diversity by learning about a famous American Indian.
- Explore causes, consequences, and possible solutions to global issues.

VOCABULARY

Introduce the vocabulary words and write them on the board. Help students find a definition for each word. Have students use each word in a sentence.

"Chief Tecumseh"

treaties	Great Spirit
productions	miserable
unite	

"Save the Rain Forests!"

canopy	dense
species	extinct
destruction	native

Tap Prior Knowledge

"Chief Tecumseh": Ask the students how they would feel if the government told them they had to leave their home. Would they be angry?

"Save the Rain Forests!": Ask the students to tell a fact they know about rain forests. Ask them what they think rain forests are like. Why is it important to save the rain forests?

Skill to Emphasize

Review the section about distinguishing facts and opinions on page 98. Tell the students to look for facts and opinions in the two articles. Facts can be proven, but opinions cannot be proven.

DURING READING

Preview Text Features

Have the students note Tecumseh's speech. A speech gives the words a person says in a public announcement. In "Save the Rain Forests!," subheadings summarize information in a section of the article. Labels tell what is shown in the illustration and graph. Boldfaced words indicate vocabulary words.

Comprehending the Selection

Model how to distinguish between facts and opinions by asking: *Which statements can be proved? Which statements cannot be proved?*

AFTER READING

Reinforce the Comprehension Skill

Ask the students to identify some facts and opinions in the article and explain how they decided which was which. Ask the students what the writers are trying to do by using opinions in the selections. In the article about Tecumseh, the speech argues that the land belongs to the Indians because they were the first on it. In the rain forest article, the writer is trying to convince the reader that the rain forests should be saved.

Distribute copies of the Fact-Opinion Chart on page 124 to help the students organize the information. Then have them complete the chart for the two articles.

Assess

Have the students complete the activities for the selections.

WRITE ABOUT IT

Distribute copies of the Fact-Opinion Chart on page 124 to the students. Have them use the chart to plan a letter on an issue they have opinions about. After they complete the chart, have them write a letter that contains both facts and opinions.

AT HOME

Have the students search through the newspaper or news magazines for articles on the rain forest and bring these articles to school to share with the class.

Chief Tecumseh

There were many American Indians who lived on land between the eastern states and the Mississippi River. In the early 1800s, many American Indian groups were forced to sign **treaties** with Governor William Henry Harrison. In these treaties, the American Indians gave their land to the United States.

Tecumseh was the chief of the Shawnee, a group of American Indians. He was very angry about the treaties. In 1810, Tecumseh met with Governor Harrison. Tecumseh told Harrison that the United States had no right to take land from American Indians. Here is part of his speech.

"Once . . . there was no white man on this continent. . . . All belonged to red men, children of the same parents, placed on it by the **Great Spirit** that made them, to keep it, . . . to enjoy its **productions**, and to fill it with the same race. Once a happy race—since made **miserable** by the white people who are never contented. . . . The way . . . to stop this evil is for all the red men to **unite** in claiming a common and equal right in the land, as it was at first . . . ; for it never was divided, but belongs to all for the use of each.

"The white people have no right to take the land from the Indians, because they had it first; it is theirs. . . . All red men have equal rights to the . . . land. It belongs to the first who sits down on his blanket or skins which he has thrown upon the ground; and till he leaves it no other has a right."

Name _____ Date _____

Comprehension and Vocabulary Review

➡ **Write F for fact or O for opinion before each statement.**

____ **1.** Tecumseh was the chief of the Shawnee.

____ **2.** "The white people have no right to take the land from the Indians."

____ **3.** The land "belongs to the first who sits down on his blanket."

____ **4.** In 1810, Tecumseh met with Governor Harrison.

____ **5.** "The way . . . to stop this evil is for all the red men to unite."

____ **6.** Many American Indian groups were forced to sign treaties.

➡ **Darken the circle by the best answer.**

7. Whom did Tecumseh say made American Indians miserable?
Ⓐ other Indians
Ⓑ the Great Spirit
Ⓒ white people
Ⓓ the Mississippi River

8. What did Tecumseh believe American Indians should do to stop white people from taking their land?
Ⓐ run away
Ⓑ unite
Ⓒ be miserable
Ⓓ throw blankets on the ground

9. A treaty is _____.
Ⓐ something good to eat
Ⓑ a kind of blanket
Ⓒ an American Indian house
Ⓓ an agreement

10. You can conclude that Tecumseh believed the land belonged to American Indians because _____.
Ⓐ they paid for it
Ⓑ they had it first
Ⓒ they had more blankets
Ⓓ they were not white

Save the Rain Forests!

What is that strange sound? It's a howler monkey calling out a warning. See that furry animal moving in slow motion? That's a three-toed sloth. What's that colorful bird? It's a toucan. Welcome to the rain forest. You won't find a more interesting place anywhere else on Earth!

Most rain forests are found near the center of Earth, or the equator. This area is called the tropics. The weather stays hot all year round. Tropical rain forests usually get between 160 and 400 inches (400–1000 centimeters) of rain each year. The rain forests may be wet, but they're also bursting with life.

Treetop Treasures

The top layer of trees in a rain forest is called the **canopy**. The canopy leaves are very **dense**. Almost no light reaches down to the floor of the rain forest because of this thick layer.

A rain forest canopy is one of the richest places on Earth. Almost half of the world's plant and animal **species** live in a jungle canopy.

How do scientists learn about rain forests? One way is by living in canopy rafts. Canopy rafts look like huge spider webs. Sometimes hot air balloons drop the rafts in place. Scientists must climb almost 100 feet (30 meters) up to get to the canopy rafts. They work and sleep in the rafts. From the rafts, scientists can get a good look at the canopy's plants and animals. They study how each one lives and grows.

Destroying Rain Forests

Rain forests are in trouble. Each day more and more of the rain forests are cut down or burned. You probably live far from a rain forest, so why should you care about them?

Rain forests are important to everyone on the planet. The plants in the rain forests make a gas in the air that we need to breathe. Rain forests also help control Earth's weather. When the trees are cut down, Earth gets hotter.

   Nonfiction Comprehension: Grades 3–4, SV 8947-8

Save the Rain Forests!, page 2

Trees are not the only things that are lost when rain forests are cut down. Many kinds of animals become **extinct**. Over 20,000 different kinds of plants and animals are destroyed each year.

We must end this **destruction**. We must share Earth with all plants and animals. I think it would be a sad world without the slow-moving sloth or the powerful jaguar.

The Outdoor Drugstore

For thousands of years, people have lived in the rain forests. These **native** people know how to use rain forest plants to keep healthy. They have learned how to use every part of the forest without destroying it. Many scientists now study with the native people of the rain forests to learn about the medicines that are found there.

It is a fact that over one fourth of our medicines come from plants. Many of these plants can be found only in rain forests. One important drug comes from a plant called periwinkle. This drug can help people who have leukemia (loo KEE mee ah) or Hodgkin's Disease.

Some people believe that the cures for many diseases may be found in rain forests. If we destroy them, we may never know. It is for this reason, and many more, that we must save the rain forests. In my view, our future depends on it.

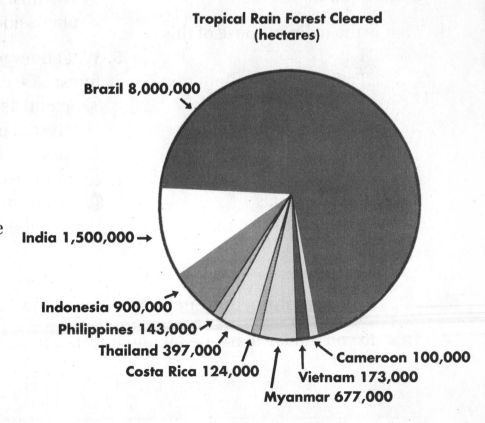

Tropical Rain Forest Cleared (hectares)

Brazil 8,000,000
India 1,500,000
Indonesia 900,000
Philippines 143,000
Thailand 397,000
Costa Rica 124,000
Myanmar 677,000
Vietnam 173,000
Cameroon 100,000

Comprehension Review

→ **Darken the circle by the best answer.**

1. How do scientists learn about rain forest medicines?
   (A) by studying with people who live in the rain forests
   (B) by collecting the rain that falls in the rain forests
   (C) by eating the plants
   (D) by watching the animals

2. What happens after rain forest trees are cut down?
   (A) Earth gets cooler.
   (B) Earth gets hotter.
   (C) Scientists discover new medicines.
   (D) The equator moves.

3. What is the main purpose of this article?
   (A) to tell a funny story about rain forests
   (B) to ask readers to protect rain forests
   (C) to tell readers about the lives of rain forest animals
   (D) to ask readers to visit rain forests

4. When a kind of animal becomes extinct, _____.
   (A) it moves somewhere else
   (B) it grows new ears
   (C) it is no longer living
   (D) it starts to eat rain forest plants

5. Which of these statements is an opinion?
   (A) Most rain forests are found near the equator.
   (B) The top layer of trees in a rain forest is called the canopy.
   (C) One important drug comes from a plant called periwinkle.
   (D) We must share Earth with all plants and animals.

6. What does <u>not</u> happen when rain forests are destroyed?
   (A) Scientists learn more about rain forest plants.
   (B) Trees are lost.
   (C) Animals become extinct.
   (D) We lose many medicines that could help cure diseases.

→ **Write complete sentences to answer the question.**

7. What do you think will happen if rain forests continue to be cut down?

_____

_____

Nonfiction Comprehension: Grades 3–4, SV 8947-8

Vocabulary Review

Write a word from the box for each definition. The letters in boxes will spell the name of a rain forest bird.

> canopy   destruction   equator   extinct   native

1. The imaginary line around the center of Earth

   ___ ___ ___ ___ [1] [2] ___

2. The act of ruining something

   ___ ___ ___ ___ [3] ___ ___ ___ ___ ___

3. No longer living

   ___ ___ ___ [4] ___ ___ ___

4. People born in a certain place

   ___ [5] ___ ___ ___ ___

5. A covering or top layer

   ___ ___ [6] ___ ___ ___ ___

Answer: ___ ___ ___ ___ ___ ___ ___

Build Your Vocabulary

Context clues are words or sentences that help you figure out the meaning of an unknown word.

Look for context clues to help you complete each sentence. Write a word from the box to complete each sentence.

> species   dense   tropics

6. The _____ leaves blocked out the sunlight.

7. In the winter, I wish I was in the warm, sunny _____.

8. Animals that belong to one _____ are all in the same special group.

Nonfiction Comprehension: Grades 3–4, SV 8947-8

Main Idea Map

Details

_____
_____
_____

_____
_____
_____

Main Idea

_____
_____
_____

_____
_____
_____
_____

_____
_____
_____
_____

Details

_____
_____
_____

_____
_____
_____

Main Idea

_____
_____
_____

_____
_____
_____

_____
_____
_____

Name _____ Date_____

Important Idea

_____
_____
_____
_____

Important Idea

_____
_____
_____
_____

Important Idea

_____
_____
_____
_____

Summary

_____
_____
_____
_____
_____
_____
_____
_____
_____
_____
_____
_____

Nonfiction Comprehension: Grades 3–4, SV 8947-8

Name _____ Date _____

Sequence Chart

Event 1
_____
_____

Event 2
_____
_____

Event 3
_____
_____

Event 4
_____
_____

Sequence Chart

Event 1
_____
_____

Event 2
_____
_____

Event 3
_____
_____

Event 4
_____
_____

Blackline Masters: Sequence
Nonfiction Comprehension: Grades 3–4, SV 8947-8

Name _____ Date _____

Cause

Effect

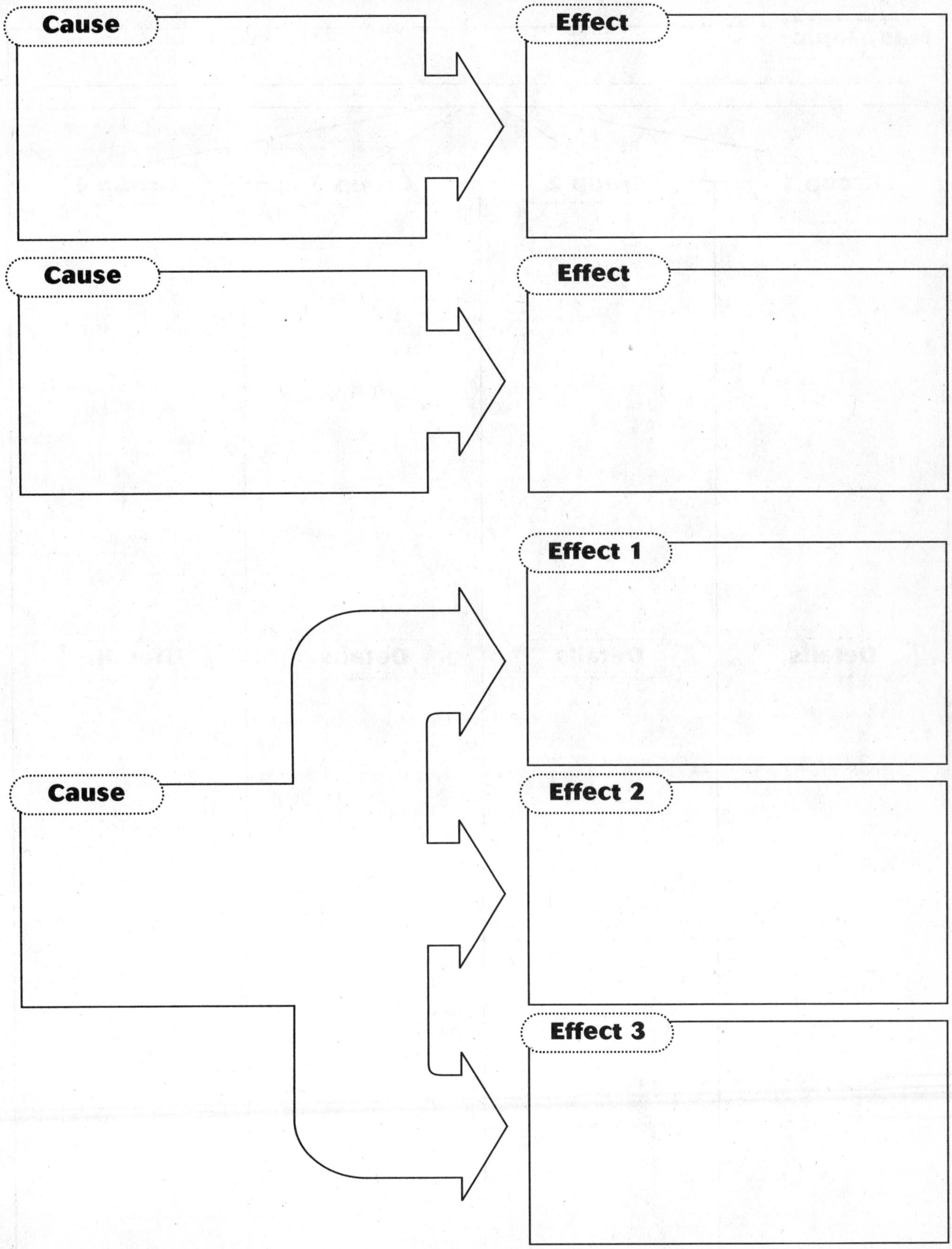

Cause

Effect

Cause

Effect 1

Effect 2

Effect 3

Name _____ Date _____

Classification Tree Diagram

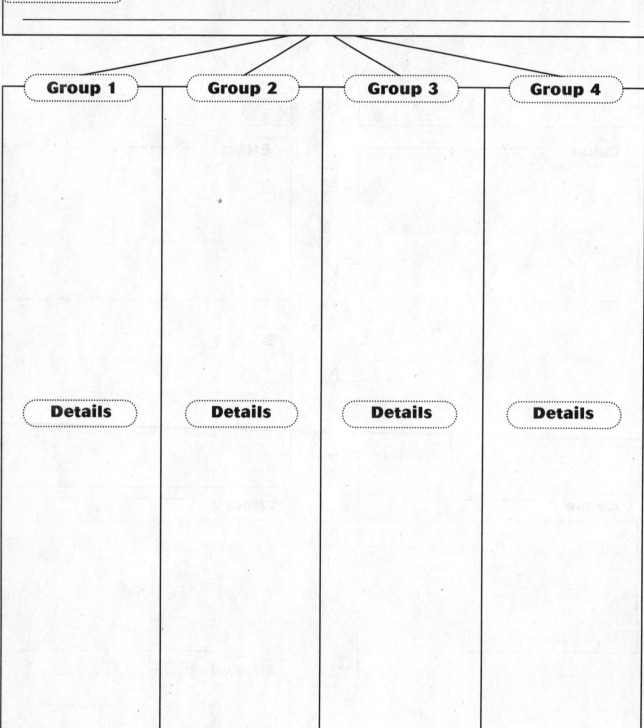

Main Topic _____

Group 1   Group 2   Group 3   Group 4

Details   Details   Details   Details

Blackline Masters: Classification
Nonfiction Comprehension: Grades 3–4, SV 8947-8

Name _____ Date _____

Venn Diagram

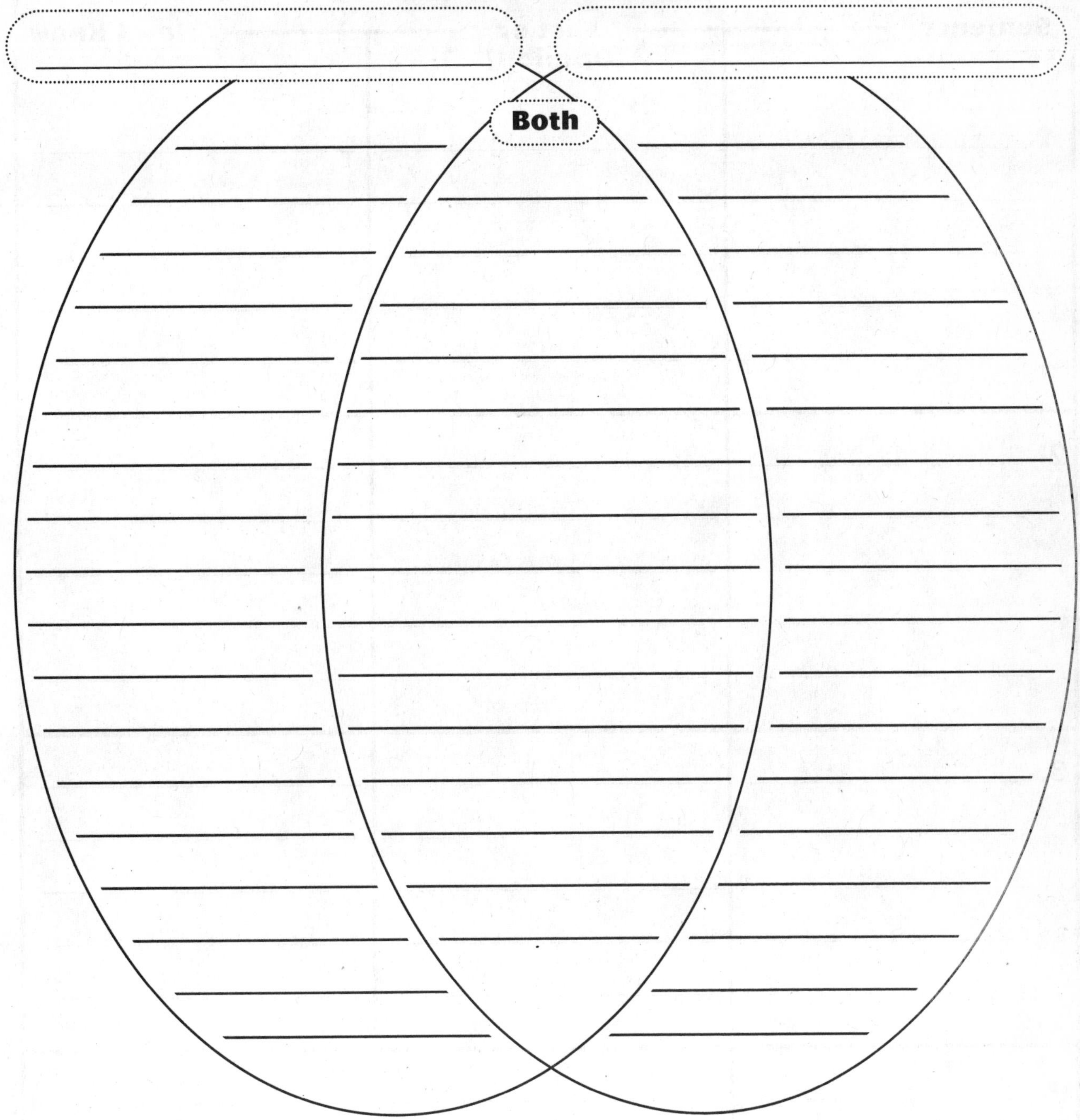

....

_____   _____

Both

_____   _____
_____   _____
_____   _____
_____   _____
_____   _____
_____   _____
_____   _____
_____   _____
_____   _____
_____   _____
_____   _____
_____   _____
_____   _____
_____   _____

Main similarities:

_____

_____

Main differences:

_____

_____

www.harcourtschoolsupply.com   **123**   **Blackline Masters: Comparison-Contrast**
© Harcourt Achieve Inc. All rights reserved.   Nonfiction Comprehension: Grades 3–4, SV 8947-8

Name _____ Date _____

Fact-Opinion Chart

Sentence	Fact or Opinion?	How I Know
1. _____ _____ _____ _____ _____	_____ _____ _____ _____ _____	_____ _____ _____ _____ _____
2. _____ _____ _____ _____ _____	_____ _____ _____ _____ _____	_____ _____ _____ _____ _____
3. _____ _____ _____ _____ _____	_____ _____ _____ _____ _____	_____ _____ _____ _____ _____
4. _____ _____ _____ _____ _____	_____ _____ _____ _____ _____	_____ _____ _____ _____ _____

Blackline Masters: Fact-Opinion
Nonfiction Comprehension: Grades 3–4, SV 8947-8

Page 8
1. B
2. C
3. D
4. A
5. B
6. D
7. B
8. C

Page 10
1. B
2. A
3. D
4. B
5. B
6. A
7. B
8. C

Page 13
1. A
2. D
3. C
4. C
5. A
6. C
7. Answers will vary. Possible response: It is more crowded and noisier, but with more things to do.

Page 15
1. C
2. C
3. B
4. A
5. B
6. A
7. Answers will vary but should indicate one of the winter months.

Page 18
1. C
2. A
3. B
4. D
5. C
6. B
7. Answers will vary but should indicate that the unused calories are stored as fat.

Page 21
1. B
2. C
3. B
4. D
5. B
6. C
7. Answers will vary but should suggest that the road map would help them to find their way in an unfamiliar place.

Page 24
1. C
2. The topic of the paragraph is the howler monkey.
3. The main idea of the paragraph is that howler monkeys are interesting animals.

Page 26
1. B
2. B
3. C
4. A
5. C
6. B
7. Answers will vary. Possible response: Goods are products that people make or grow, but services are jobs that people do to help other people.

Page 28
1. The news article is about Dan Edwards.
2. Dan Edwards won a new car.
3. He won the car last Wednesday.
4. He won the car at the mall.
5. Dan won the car by naming all the Presidents of the United States.

Page 30
1. B
2. C
3. B
4. B
5. D
6. B
7. Answers will vary. Possible response: The carousel is fun for both parents and children because the adults can relax and the children can have good, old-fashioned fun.

Page 32
1. C
2. B
3. C
4. B
5. C
6. D
7. Answers will vary but should include transportation, recreation, production of electricity, and sources of drinking water.

Page 33
1. river
2. source
3. banks
4. mouth
5. tributary
6. bed
7. The river keeps all its money in its banks.

Page 35
A government can raise money by collecting taxes, charging fees, or borrowing money.

Nonfiction Comprehension: Grades 3–4, SV 8947-8

Page 36
1. B
2. C
3. C
4. A

Summary: Answers will vary. Possible response: A government offers goods and services to the people it represents. To offer these goods and services, the government must have money. It gets this money by collecting taxes, charging fees, or borrowing money.

Page 39
1. B
2. A
3. C
4. D

Summary: Answers will vary. Possible response: Natural events, such as earthquakes, thunderstorms, and blizzards, can be very dangerous. Knowing a few rules about safety can keep people from harm in these events. Knowing what to do and where to go in each disaster can mean the difference between life and death.

Page 40
1. disaster
2. prone
3. wind-chill factor
4. shelter
5. prevent
6. interior
7. appliances
8. crouch

Page 44
1. C
2. D
3. C
4. A
5. B
6. B
7. A
8. C

Page 46
Correct sequence: 4, 5, 3, 2, 1

Page 47
1. C
2. B
3. A
4. C
5. A
6. C
7. B
8. D

Page 49
1. Answers will vary.
2. Answers will vary but should be roughly 385,000 km or 240,000 miles.

Page 50
1. C
2. A
3. B
4. C
5. D
6. Answers will vary.

Page 52
Order of steps: 3, 5, 1, 6, 2, 4, 7
1. C
2. B
3. A
4. B

Page 56
1. B
2. C
3. D
4. A
5. Answers will vary. Possible response: Monarch butterflies lay their eggs on milkweed leaves, and the caterpillars that hatch eat the leaves of the milkweed plant. If the butterflies go at the wrong time, they cannot reproduce.
6. Answers will vary. Possible response: After the eggs are laid, a caterpillar hatches from each egg. The caterpillar eats the milkweed leaves and grows quickly. It sheds its skin several times. After the last shedding, the caterpillar forms a chrysalis around its body. The butterfly forms inside the chrysalis. After 14 days, the adult butterfly emerges.

Page 57
1. habitat
2. nectar
3. molt
4. chrysalis
5. solitary
6. migration
7. cluster; A
8. emerges; A

Page 60
1. C
2. C
3. D
4. B
5. C
6. B
7. Answers will vary. Possible response: Rain can loosen soil and wash it into a river. Moving water can cut away the banks of a river.

Page 62
1. C
2. B
3. A
4. D
5. changes the way the body works
6. slow down the nervous system
7. too many drugs at one time
8. speed up the nervous system

Page 65
1. C
2. D
3. B
4. A
5. When Dr. Welch saw that the child had diphtheria, he was very worried because he knew the boy could die and others could get the disease.
6. Planes couldn't fly at this time because the high winds and cold temperatures prevented the planes from flying.
7. Seppala decided to take the shortcut across frozen water because he knew that he could save valuable time by going that way.
8. The dogs' paws began to bleed because they were cut by the pieces of ice.

Page 66
1. A
2. C
3. D
4. A
5. D
6. B
7. C
8. A

Page 70
1. C
2. B
3. D
4. B
5. B
6. A

Descriptions will vary. Possible response: Starfish have a small body with a mouth on the bottom side. Most starfish have five arms that stick out from their bodies, but some have more than 25 arms. Stiff spines cover their bodies and arms. Starfish are often dull yellow or orange, but they can be bright colors. Starfish can be as small as 1/2 inch wide and as big as 3 feet wide.

Page 72
1. B
2. C
3. D
4. A
5. B
6. C
7. C
8. D

Page 74
1. C
2. A
3. D
4. C
5. B
6. A
7. Answers may vary. Possible response: Chief Joseph said he wanted time to look for his children and see how many he could find.

Page 77
1. B
2. C
3. D
4. C
5. B
6. A
7. The job of the leaves of a tree is to make food for the tree.

Page 78
1. grows straight down into the soil
2. system of roots that spread out
3. hard, woody stem of a tree
4. tough outside layer of a tree
5. full of tubes that carry water and minerals
6. mixture of water and minerals in a tree
7. grows between the bark and the sapwood
8. oldest and hardest wood in the tree
9. **and 10.** Sentences will vary.

Page 80
1. D
2. A
3. D
4. B
5. D
6. B
7. People live on the crust of Earth.

Page 81
1. at the very center of Earth
2. is hot liquid metal
3. the thickest layer
4. makes up continents and ocean floors
5. Sentences will vary. Possible response: The inner core is very hot, solid, about 800 miles thick, and made of iron and nickel.
6. Sentences will vary. Possible response: The outer core is made of hot liquid iron and nickel and is about 1,400 miles thick.
7. Sentences will vary. Possible response: The mantle is about 1,800 miles thick and has several layers.
8. Sentences will vary. Possible response: The crust is the outer layer of Earth and is about 5 to 20 miles thick.

Page 85
1. C
2. A
3. D
4. B
5. C
6. B
7. Answers will vary. Possible response: Two factors that affect the climate of an area are its latitude and its nearness to ocean currents.

Page 86
Check the students' tree diagrams for the correct names of the climate zones and details that apply to each. The climate zone that students live in may vary but will probably be the temperate zone.

Page 88
1. C
2. B
3. D
4. B
5. A
6. B
7. C
8. A

Page 90
1. Probability is the chance that an event will happen.
2. Independent and dependent probability are different.
3. Answers will vary. Possible response: Independent probability deals with details that do not change. Dependent probability deals with changing details. Independent probably is not determined by something else, but dependent probability is.

Page 92
1. D
2. A
3. C
4. C
5. D
6. D
7. B
8. B

Page 95
1. B
2. C
3. D
4. B
5. B
6. B
7. Answers will vary. Possible response: The frill makes the lizard look bigger and scarier than it really is.

Page 96
1. predator
2. prey
3. grasp
4. sway
5. crest
6. camouflage
7. d
8. b
9. c
10. a

Page 97
Check the students' Venn diagrams to be sure they have included details about the lizards under the proper headings. Possible responses:
Frilled Lizard: fast runner; opens mouth wide; looks big to stay safe
Veiled Chameleon: moves slowly; long, curly tail; changes color to stay safe
Both: scales; shed skin; lie in sunlight to warm their bodies
1. Answers will vary. Possible response: Both lizards eat insects and lie in the sunlight to warm themselves.
2. Answers will vary. Possible response: The lizards look different and have different ways to protect themselves.

Page 101
1. B
2. A
3. C
4. A
5. B
6. D
7. A
8. B

Page 104
1. C
2. B
3. C
4. C
5. Many child workers lost their lives in factory fires because the owners locked the doors and the workers could not escape.
6. Factory owners hated to see Kelley coming because she ordered them to stop using child workers.
7. Kelley made factory owners burn thousands of dollars worth of clothes because they might have smallpox germs on them.

Page 105
1. A
2. D
3. B
4. A
5. C
6. A
7. D
8. B

Page 109
1. D
2. A
3. C
4. B
5. C
6. B
7. C
8. B

Page 110
1. C
2. A
3. D
4. B
Paragraphs will vary but should include details from the article.

Page 113
1. F
2. O
3. O
4. F
5. O
6. F
7. C
8. B
9. D
10. B

Page 116
1. A
2. B
3. B
4. C
5. D
6. A
7. Answers will vary but could include points about global warming, extinction of plants and animals, and loss of medicines.

Page 117
1. equator
2. destruction
3. extinct
4. native
5. canopy
Answer: toucan
6. dense
7. tropics
8. species

Reference
Fountas, I.C. and G.S. Pinnell. 2001. *Guiding Readers and Writers: Grades 3–6.* Portsmouth, NH: Heinemann.